THE FERMENTING UNIVERSE

THE FERMENTING UNIVERSE

Myths of Eternal Change

J. McKim Malville

THE SEABURY PRESS · NEW YORK

The author gratefully acknowledges the permission of Harcourt Brace
Jovanovich, Inc. and Faber & Faber Ltd. in reprinting selections of
T. S. Eliot's "East Coker," "The Dry Salvages," "Burnt Norton" and
"Little Gidding" from Four Quartets, copyright, 1943, by T. S.
Eliot, copyright, 1971, by Esme Valerie Eliot.

1981
The Seabury Press
815 Second Avenue
New York, New York 10017

Printed in the United States of America

Library of Congress Cataloging in Publication Data
Malville, J McKim.   The fermenting universe.
Bibliography.
1.   Change (in religion, folklore, etc.)
2.   Cosmology.   I. Title.   II. Series.
BL325.C48M34   113   78-4078   ISBN 0-8164-2345-8

Contents

Preface

All that lives on the surface of our planet exists because of the departure of the local universe from a state of equilibrium. None dramatizes that departure quite as well as the tree, balanced precariously upon its roots, feeding upon both earth and sky. Often used as an image of the universe itself, the symbol of the Cosmic Tree unites pairs of opposites: not just heaven and earth, but movement and stillness, and life and death.

The story of the First Adam took place near a tree as death and knowledge were brought into the world. The Second Adam died on a tree giving eternal life to humankind. In Icelandic cosmology the World Ash, Yggdrasil, is the unmoving pivot of the revolving heavens. The World Eagle perches on its top and the Cosmic Serpent gnaws at its roots. Its limbs spread over the world and reach the heavens, while its roots penetrate the abyss beneath. This is the tree upon which the god Odin once hanged himself for nine days as a sacrifice to himself. And beneath the Cosmic Tree, the preserver and maintainer of the universe, Vishnu, plays as a divine child.

The Cosmic Tree, rooted in the darkness of planet Earth with the golden bird of the sun clinging to its upper branches, represents the power and paradox of a worldwide mythic image. The creative energies of a universe, expanding and fecund but also limited and dying, are expressed in that mythic image. Much of our scientific cosmology can be viewed as communal myth building, expressing, often much too obscurely, what are the highest admirations of our culture: the beauty, vitality, depth, and interrelatedness of our world. Too rarely, it seems, can we penetrate the details of our science to see those basic intuitions which have emerged unconsciously during the construction of a scientific theory. With this book, I hope to illumine some of those life affirming insights as they appear in today's physics and cosmology.

Etched deeply into the face of the cosmos is eternal change. It penetrates so thoroughly the matter and energy of the universe that perhaps the ultimate meaning of our lives may be perceived in the promise of change. The universe is out of balance; that is the fundamental fact of our existence. Ever seeking equilibrium the universe moves, and out of that movement we have emerged, the improbable children of change.

Change is our essence. We do not revere stasis or worship that which is stagnant. Whatever sacred quality there is to our lives is to a great extent dependent upon the powers of change which nudge and tickle and spur us into action. It is a supreme mystery that the ever-changing should be ever so good and ever so enjoyable.

An enduring symbol of eternal change is the fire of Heraclites. For him all forms of matter were but evanescent stages in the ever-flickering flame. The ocean with its many voices and its cosmic rhythms is another such symbol, as is the turning wheel possessing stillness at its center. These symbols are gathered together in one of the great modern explorations of time and change, *The Four Quartets* of T. S. Eliot. For what I hope are obvious reasons, I use passages from *The Four Quartets* as epigraphs for each of the chapters. Eliot's metaphors create a remarkably effective and sturdy bridge between the two cultures of today.

THE FERMENTING UNIVERSE
Myths of Eternal Change

1. All Things Flow: Nothing Abides

Old stone to new building, old timber to new fires,
Old fires to ashes, and ashes to the earth
Which is already flesh, fur and faeces,
Bone of man and beast, cornstalk and leaf.

T. S. Eliot, "East Coker"

Today we are confronted by the extraordinary spectacle of modern man at the focus of three thousand years of knowledge and experience, yet no less uneasy with himself and no more comfortable in his universe than his predecessors. To a tragic degree the average man has gained very little from the explosive growth of knowledge and technology in the last century. His universe actually seems more alien and more unfamiliar than ever before. He feels frequently dehumanized and despiritualized by his technology which has only brought him nervous breakdowns, sleeping pills, and gadgets.

The forces of modern technology pull in different directions. They fragment rather than integrate. Technology seemingly can only pollute the air and water. For most of us technology has not provided any significant increase in insight into ourselves nor understanding of our universe. It is indeed a tragic irony, for such insight and understanding is most certainly contained in modern science. But, because of the fracturing of our lives, we have been unable to gain true advantage from the knowledge which is unfolding around us.

One of the strong and pervasive images of the twentieth century western world is that man is alone in an alien universe, absurd in his inability to participate in the vast schemes of the cosmos, a fluke, a mistake, perhaps even a cosmic joke. That such an image should find a firm foothold in the west speaks poignantly of the terror and unease with which many non-scientists in the west view the current state of science and technology. Many spectators of the advance of western science are simply overwhelmed by the increasing complexity of the universe which seems day by day to become more and more unfamiliar and certainly more bizarre.

That such a view is so pervasive today is a tragedy, part of the deeper tragedy of the separation of man from his environment. Man has seemingly forgotten the roots of his existence, roots which sink not just into the soil of his homeland, but into the elementary particles, quanta, and galaxies which make up our reality. What is desperately needed now is all the poetic imagery and creative imagination of mankind to carry us to a new and more valid understanding of man's role in the cosmos.

Guided by recent discoveries in the physical sciences we have moved into a new reality in the twentieth century which can only be described as opulent. At the heart of that opulence lies unrelenting change. Many of the old immutables of the universe have been dissolved in the fires of quantum mechanics, relativity, and cosmology and have been replaced by a microcosm which changes in rhythm with the changing macrocosm. Today in astronomy and physics there is an almost unprecedented sense of excitement and anticipation as we discover a violence and power in the night sky which we had not foreseen.

Change penetrates so deeply into the matter and energy of the universe that the ultimate meaning of our lives may be perceived in the promise of perpetual newness. Yet, how rarely do we appreciate our world's extraordinary and so very necessary vitality. For instance, the most fundamental quality of our universe is the continuing expansion of space and the consequent departure of its contents from equilibrium and stability. Were the universe not expanding we would not be around to ask cosmic questions or to be amazed and puzzled. Were the universe not out of equilibrium, the improbables like you and me, the giraffe and the rhinoceros would certainly not be present. Only a dull, warm broth of matter and energy would inhabit the universe.

On the following pages I explore some of the physics and mythology, our human attempts at describing the aliveness of the yeasty and beautiful universe which we inhabit. My intent is to present a view of the restlessness of the world from the vantage point of modern physics and astronomy, placing that view, whenever possible, within the perspective of the mythologies of our species.

We have often viewed ourselves as human objects having emerged from inhuman mud. Surrounded thus by the moat of our humanness, we seem alone in the universe, sharing perhaps a little with the other living creatures on this planet, but certainly nothing with the physical processes occurring in stars and galaxies. A stranger and a tourist in the physical universe, we contribute little other than our refuse and receive little other than an earth upon which to stand.

In such a dichotomized cosmos in which man and nonman represent opposite poles, our experience on this earth is similar to a visit paid to a barren tree by a flock of wandering starlings who rest momentarily on its dead branches before flying off. They do not know from where they have come nor do they know where they shall go next. They only know that the ancient tree is their current perch. The tree is not another starling; it is lifeless and therefore means nothing to them. The tree has indeed very little to offer them in terms of nourishment, shelter, or instruction.

Before the twentieth century, the primary mission of physics was that of attempting to identify the permanent stuff of which the dead tree was made, and then to discover the laws which this stuff is obliged to follow.

With the development of relativity and quantum mechanics our quest has altered direction as the permanent things of the world now look much less permanent. No longer does it appear useful to describe the physical world in terms of permanent objects and immutable laws. Rather, our universe now has the appearance of a continuous field of changing patterns. We are a wine skin in which the still fermenting contents slosh back and forth. Ours is not a cosmic archive in which everything preserved within its rigid walls is protected from change, for there are no isolated items to protect.

Such is our current myth, built of the dreams of physicists, mathematicians, and biologists; a myth, so fully lived today that we are reluctant to identify it as one. But myth it is: today's affirmation of change and promise of surprise. And, as with all myths before it, sometime in the not too far distant future, it will suffer dismemberment as new experiences and vision replace the old.

It may appear that physicists have been slow to abandon the myth of atoms, the changeless and fundamental building blocks of physical reality. They still seem to be searching for elementary particles. But these particles for which they search are much more complex and subtle than the hard and indestructible atoms which Democritus envisioned. The mesons, leptons, and hadrons of the subatomic world are more like loose knots on a rope which can be moved back and forth than marbles; more like candle flames than glass encased light bulbs.

In fact, these so-called elementary particles are not too unlike ourselves, for what are we but patterns of flowing air, water, and food? Matter and energy pass through us as we constantly discard old atoms and add new ones, and we have the most uncanny ability to retain our shape and appearance. Always changing in substance, the basic human pattern manages to remain intact for a few score years.

What indeed is there in this cosmic ocean of ours which is not changing in some way? We have been discovering in astronomy during the last few decades that change is a characteristic of the universe beyond the earth. Our sun rises each day appearing the same, but each day it is a different sun. Every morning our sun is less of a sun than it was the day before, for some of its matter has been sacrificed and converted into that energy upon which we earthlings so completely rely. Some four million tons of matter per second are lost by the sun as it destroys itself so that we might live on our planet.

Other stars, such as the blue giant Rigel in the constellation of Orion change even more rapidly, annihilating ten-thousand times more matter every second than our sun. This matter pours out of the star into the thirsty, cold space which surrounds it, never to return, at least not while the universe is still expanding. As a consequence, Rigel can continue transforming its matter for only some tens of millions of years.

Our sun (bless it) has a stable lifetime lasting perhaps 8 to 10 billion years. The galaxy contains some 100 billion stars, visible to us only because they are destroying matter; every year in our galaxy an amount of matter exceeding 2,000 earths is transformed into radiation to flow and diffuse through space.

Our galaxy is still fertile and in huge clouds of matter such as the great nebula of Orion, new stars are constantly being born, which rise up, flare only briefly as judged by cosmic standards and then fall back like a burned cinder of a sky rocket to the obscurity of dark matter. New stars, new planets, perhaps even new galaxies, come into being while old generations pass out of existence.

The galaxy tumbles and spins among the 15 other galaxies which make up our local cluster of galaxies; our cluster and hundreds of millions of other clusters in the universe expand away fom each other as the rubbery structure of space-time continues to stretch. Stars may destroy themselves as they flash into visibility as supernovae in ours, and in distant galaxies. Entire galaxies may maim themselves as they explosively throw out matter in the form of dust, gas, and stars. We know of two galaxies which have experienced violent explosions in their centers during the last 100 million years. Perhaps all galaxies pass through such an explosive phase. Even our own relatively quiet galaxy shows some evidence of violence in its central regions as clouds of hydrogen gas are being expelled from its center with speeds of 50 km/sec.

The apparently permanent features of our planet are always changing. Giant plates of crustal material buckle on the ocean floor and continents drift apart. Rock mountains are worn down by water and torn apart by heat and wind. The life which clings to the surface of this changing, wobbling rock of Earth is in a state of continual change. In our bodies cells constantly die and are replaced by new ones. Every seven years we are completely replaced. Species mutate, flourish, and die. The sky changes, aurorae dance in the polar skies, shadows rush across the earth's surface while the ground shudders and fractures.

Beneath our feet at the atomic level there is universal and ceaseless motion which becomes more violent the deeper we penetrate. Molecules vibrate and rotate, their electrons caught in ceaseless motion. Individual electrons flicker due to quantum mechanical effects, dancing to unheard melodies. The entire structure of space-time shakes and at the smallest level we can conceive, it appears that our reality is continually dissolving and reforming. Even the old constants of our physical laws are suspect; the constant of gravity or the mass of the proton may change while the universe expands and contracts.

No feature of our universe has been discovered which does not undergo some form of metamorphosis. Every fiber and droplet of the universe seems to be caught up in a continual reprocessing. These transformations are not merely imposed upon essentially immutable matter; rather they are built into the very nature of matter. One cannot discuss matter separate from change, for matter would not be our matter were it not changing matter.

Surrounded as we are by stars and mountains which do not appear to change during our lifetimes, it is exceedingly hard to grasp the transitional nature of our reality. Let us try a little exercise involving the medium of the motion picture. It is not a bad analogy to liken ourselves and our experiences to one frame of a movie, frozen into immobility by our limited consciousness. Our psychological present is about ten years in duration: the period of intense memory. Beyond those ten years we begin to seem different people living in a different world. In each celluloid chip we see ourselves as stable objects embedded in a ten-year tableau.

The movie known as *Our Universe* has already lasted about 15 billion years. Thus there are already more than one billion frames each 10 years long in our own movie. In a typical three-hour movie there are about 250,000 frames, and it is hence no wonder at all that we have such difficulty placing ourselves in the proper perspective in our universe. Take any full-length movie and in your imagination try to figure out what the movie is all about on the basis of one single frame cut out of the reel. You might even collect a few other frames on either side of yours and then talk to other people who have studied frames ten or twenty steps away from yours. Look at your frames carefully with a microscope. You may study the arrangement of the crystals of silver nitrate with an electron microscope and investigate the layers of gelatin upon the celluloid backing. You may even wish to ignite your little chip of film and subject the ashes to chemical analysis. But the task of determining the nature of the movies remains child's play compared to that of understanding the cosmic movie. With its billions of frames the universe contains at least a factor of 4,000 more items to be investigated with many more subtleties and nuances than can be captured on a reel of celluloid.

Caught in our moving world, with horror of having nothing permanent to cling to, but with exultation at the promise of unending newness, we thus encounter change wherever we look. As a symbol, it is as deep as the roots of western civilization, first having been explored in detail by Heraclites about 500 B.C. Feeding on the wild grasses and plants of the mountains of Ephesus, disdaining the life of the city, Heraclites created a remarkably enduring philosophy of eternal change built upon the imagery of eternal fire. Water and earth are but transient aspects of the ceaseless metamorphosis of flame. "This world . . . was made neither by a god nor by man, but was and is and shall be ever-living Fire, in measures being kindled and in measures going out." Bearing a remarkable resemblance to our modern views of the birth and death of the universe or of the origin of our solar system, Heraclites's Fire moves both "upwards" or "downwards" condensing to form water and earth, or dispersing as earth and water return to fire. "The upward path and the downward path is one and the same." Condensation and evaporation alternate in an endless cycle of creation and destruction, and the Eternal Fire ever flickers as flame consumes and overcomes the ponderous and static world.

The many aspects of the world are reconciled in the imagery of changing tongues of flame which are "always ceasing to be what they were and becoming what they will be." Heraclites is best known for his famous river which is ever changing: "You can not step twice into the same river for other waters are ever flowing on to you."

The universe and everything within it are caught up in the eternal process of becoming in which man is as ephemeral as the candle flame "kindled and put out like a light in the night." Change is indeed a blessing for "in change one finds rest; it is weariness to be always toiling at the same things and always beginning afresh."

As in the philosophy of the *I Ching*, Heraclites identifies the presence of opposites as vital to the continuation of the world. All of the Yin and Yang are but moments in the fluctuating fire. Each one is necessary to the meaning and existing of its opposite and our world needs both as the pulling and straining of a violin string needs its tension in order to produce music. "From things that differ comes the fairest attunement." Throughout his philosophy eternal fire is described as the indestructible energy of the world, the infinitely generous source of all the variety of the universe.

Eternal fire, the ultimate source of the world, must be perceived in the contraries of change. Awareness that opposites are merely different aspects of the same source is the chief escape from the endlessly repeating millennia.

We know more of Heraclites's death than his life. In life, the recluse avoided people and cities and must have brooded alone in the mountains over his fire circle. His death is described by Diogenes Laertius:

> And at last becoming a complete misanthrope, he used to spend his time walking about the mountains, feeding on grasses and plants; and in consequence of these habits he was attacked by the dropsy, and so he returned to the city, and asked the physicians, in a riddle, whether they were able to produce a drought after wet weather. And as they did not understand him, he shut himself up in a stable for oxen, and covered himself with cow dung, hoping to cause the wet to evaporate from him by the warmth that this produced. And as he did himself no good in this way, he died, having lived seventy years.

This vision of eternal change which was first given voice by the Greek recluse of 500 B.C. finds expression in the modern world in the philosophy of Bergson, the writing of Kazantzakis, and the theology of Teilhard de Chardin. We see it mirrored in the astrophysics of the oscillating universe swinging from fireball of creation to fireball of destruction. The Heraclitean viewpoint is found in modern quantum mechanics in which the "things" of the world are described as changing probability functions and in relativity theory in which objects become nothing more than tubes through which flow smaller tubes and smaller tubes, ad infinitum.

Our world of changing probability functions and intermingling world tubes would perhaps be more familiar to Heraclites than it is to most of us who live in the twentieth century. Were Heraclites to return as another Rip Van Winkle he would probably recognize his river and his fire appropriately transformed by the intervening millennia of human experience and would perhaps remark, "The details of your science are a little bewildering. Your quarks, atoms, and quasars are magnificent discoveries which I don't yet comprehend. But I understand the essential idea: all things flow."

2. *Space-Time Tubes*

The river is within us, the sea is all about us.
T. S. Eliot, "The Dry Salvages"

Before returning to the Heraclitean river of the present we lived inside a Newtonian myth for three centuries. It was a remarkably neat and stable reality we had created for ourselves. Inside the world was clean, well-lighted, and predictable; during those centuries the precise working of the well-oiled cosmic clock was joy and a wonder to behold.

God was to be complimented, so clever to have created such a well-designed machine. For that matter, man was clever for having discovered the blueprints. The ocean tides, the falling apple, and orbiting planets were all ruled by Newton's laws. All the complex variety contained by the universe could be understood by his mathematical short-hand and by those concepts of energy, mass, and force which were his inventions. Today, Newton's synthesis is still remarkably good. Except for a handful of phenomena in the astronomers' solar system and in the physicists' laboratory, we still seem to dance to the tune of Newton's laws.

The laws of Newton proclaimed that the universe was eternal and free of change. Perhaps matter would alter its form, but the basic laws of motion and gravity would never change, nor alter nor decay. No surprises were allowed in this universe. A man with knowledge of the location and velocities of all the particles in the universe would be as a god for all the future would be known to him. The cosmic machine designed by Newton was so flawless and so predictable that the future in all its minutest detail was determined by the present, just as the present had been fully determined by the past.

As humans living in the Newtonian clock we were, in a sense, as changeless as the matter and energy of which we were composed. No longer were we free agents as our future and our present had been established long ago by the organization of matter and energy which had existed at the beginning of the universe.

We lost our freedom, but in return the laws of Newton showed us unsuspected wonders by pointing our sights we might have missed. Occasionally an apparent slip was discovered and it appeared possible that those laws were not as infallible as they seemed. But, for 200 years those apparent "errors" turned out to be illusory and served to increase the credibility of Newton's vision and to teach us more about the world.

The first serious confrontation between the universe and Isaac Newton occurred in the latter part of the seventeenth century when the Danish astronomer Ole Roemer had the idea of using the positions of the four brightest moons of Jupiter as a much-needed timepiece for shipboard navigators. When he investigated their positions around Jupiter carefully, he found their motions to be surprisingly erratic. Sometimes they were eight minutes faster than the orbit predicted by Newton's laws and sometimes eight minutes slower.

Moons should do better than that. Newton's laws did not allow any such sloppy behavior. Either the laws were wrong or there was an unsuspected culprit lurking somewhere in the solar system. Roemer was drawn to the latter possibility and was guided by this disagreement between theory and observation into discovering that the speed of light was not infinitely large. If the light from the moons of Jupiter does not travel instantaneously to our planet, then the moons should appear behind schedule when Jupiter is farthest from the earth. Roemer was able to estimate that the speed of light was 210,000 km/sec., only low by 30% from the best current value.

Thus did Newtonian gravity increase in reputation. So

precisely did it apply to physical phenomena that any departures indicated the presence of a previously undetected process. A situation similar to that associated with sloppy moons of Jupiter occurred in connection with the orbit of Uranus, the next planet beyond Saturn. Uranus had been discovered by the German-English astronomer William Herschel in 1781. Within ten years an orbit had been calculated which indicated that all was not well with Newtonian gravity. Even after allowance had been made from the gravitational influences of Jupiter and Saturn, it was found that Uranus did move along its predicted orbit. By the year 1840 the discrepancy between the observed positions of Uranus and those predicted from its calculated orbit had grown into a serious challenge to the accuracy of the law of gravity.

The outcome of this challenge involves a curious episode in the history of astronomy: two mathematicians almost simultaneously predicted that another planet more distant from the sun than Uranus was responsible for its apparent mis-behavior. In 1843 John Adams had just completed his work in mathematics at Cambridge and begun an analysis of the irregularities of the motion of Uranus. Three years later he sent a prediction of an eighth planet of the solar system to the Astronomer Royal of England, Sir George Airy. The Astronomer Royal did not know Adams and did not believe such a young mathematician could be successful in finding a new planet, and so before investing any time in a planet search he sent Adams a simple mathematical problem as a test for his mathematical abilities. Adams did not bother to respond, and Airy consequently let the whole matter drop.

Meanwhile in France, another mathematician, Urbian Leverrier, was working on the same problem, unaware of the work of Adams. He published his prediction of the new planet in 1846 and his prediction agreed within 1° to that of Adams. This remarkable agreement did not pass unnoticed by the Astronomer Royal but he still was not ready to rush into any reckless planet hunt. So again he sent off a test problem. This time Leverrier replied and indeed passed the test. The Cambridge Observatory was assigned the task of searching for the planet but, fumbling, failed to find it. Leverrier then decided to give the German astronomers a chance and sent his prediction to the Berlin Observatory. On the evening of the same day in September 1846 that the prediction was received, the planet was found by the Berlin Observatory less than a degree from Leverrier's prediction. The challenge to gravity had led not to its demise, but instead to a new planet.

In the early part of this century another planet hunt became necessary because Uranus was still behaving badly: even after the effects of Neptune had been taken into account, a small discrepancy still remained between prediction and observation. Gravity was being put to increasingly severe tests as observations became more precise. The search this time was undertaken at the observatory which Percival Lowell had built for the purpose of studying the canals of Mars. Lowell had calculated an orbit for planet "X" on the basis of its presumed gravitational influence upon Uranus and beginning in 1906 until the time of his death in 1916 he searched extensively for the planet. Lowell did not find evidence for a dying civilization on Mars, but he was responsible for the discovery, albeit posthumously, of the planet Pluto which carries his initials as its first two letters. In 1929 after investigating some two million stars, an assistant at the Lowell Observatory, Clyde Tombaugh, found planet "X" lying within six degrees of the position predicted by Lowell.

With remarkable success Newton's gravity stretched its thin fingers beyond our solar system to other stars revolving around each other, to stars orbiting the centers of galaxies, and to galaxies moving around the center of mass of a cluster of galaxies. Gravity became the key to understanding the dynamics of the universe. Distances of tens of millions of light years were involved in this successful outreach of gravity from one object to another. And always it worked!

How could anyone dare argue against such an overwhelmingly successful model of the world: a force of gravity F, two masses m and M, a constant of gravity G, and a distance squared accounted for it all. Not only was it totally correct but it was also astonishingly simple. The principle of gravity could be expressed in just a few unambiguous words. It was as simple as $F = mMG/r^2$. In its simplicity it had great beauty. Our world acquired reflected beauty in its ability to obey such a simple and elegant little law.

Newtonian gravity succeeded on all counts: accuracy in prediction, beauty in simplicity, and completeness in describing the universe. The inevitable consequence of such success was the transformation of the world into a Newtonian world. The model became indistinguishable with reality itself. Space, matter, and time became as Newton imagined them: separate and autonomous. Space was flat, as figured in the mind of his creator. Flatness indeed seemed another aspect of divine perfection. As a bonus, the geometry discovered by Euclid was valid in flat space.

Through the straight corridors of space moved rocks and planets. They were rigid and lonely objects which traveled along straight lines in the absence of an external force acting upon them. If they did not follow straight lines then an analysis of their motion should reveal what forces were present. The entire cosmos could thus be analyzed and dissected into separate parts. Once those forces were identified, the positions of the particles established, and their motions measured, the laws should be sufficiently accurate to describe all future developments in the universe.

All events were connected together in a unique fashion. The future was completely determined by the present as the present had been determined by the past. A particular cause produced a specific event at a later time. A modification of one part of the universe generated an effect which propagated to all parts of the universe. But, most significantly, that effect did not propagate as a wave in an ocean sweeps toward the shore or as a wave moves in the vibrating violin string. The transfer of the effect to successively more distant parts of the universe took place through the action of one discrete *thing* upon another discrete *thing*. Isolated bits of matter acted upon other isolated bits of matter.

According to the Newtonian model, there is no continuous field of gravity filling space between objects, like Jell-o filling the space between chunks of fruit. Space is empty and across that empty space there is an "action-at-a-distance" between neighboring objects. The force of gravity is transmitted instantaneously from one body to another. As soon as an object such as a moon located itself at some point in space near the earth, it somehow "knew" that the earth was there. There were nagging problems concerning the exact nature of the "force" of gravity and the details of this instantaneous action-at-a-distance between particles. But physics was meant only as a description and not as an explanation, and Newtonian gravity was an effective and efficient description of the behavior of moving matter.

Then relativity and its revolution arrived. We tend to underplay the significance of the events which occurred at the beginning of this century when Einstein "made corrections" to Newton. He did much more than merely correct. One kind of completely furnished world was discarded and was replaced by another. In its fundamental assumptions Newtonian physics is inconsistent with Einstein's theory of relativity. Both cannot be correct. Even though we should have departed from the Newtonian world more than fifty years ago, we still tend to treat ourselves and our friends as Newtonian objects, isolated from each other and able to act upon each other from a safe distance.

Our ordinary lives have been strangely unaffected by the revolution wrought by relativity. Every day it seems that we unconsciously and automatically reaffirm our Newtonian pre-conceptions. The separation of space, time, and matter are great conveniences with which we find it difficult to part. But the world is different from what it was 100 years ago, just as the world was changed as Copernicus moved the earth away from the center of the universe.

Fundamental to Einstein's theory is the proposition that there is a speed limit in our universe: no material, no message, no information can travel through space faster than the speed of light. Just as we fail to notice the highway patrol when traveling below the speed limit, so we fail to notice the effects of relativity when we are traveling much slower than the speed of light. But when a particle begins to approach that speed limit phenomena begin to occur which prevent it from going much faster. These phenomena are associated with the need for any object to have an internal communication network sufficient for it to remain aware of itself.

We humans are held together by signals which move back and forth across our body just as an army is held together by its messengers. In our atoms, the protons and electrons are bound together by electric fields. Our molecules are joined with other molecules, our muscle fibers are attached to cartilage, and our ankle bones are connected to our knee bones by this same glue of electric fields. However, changes in those electric fields cannot move faster than the speed of light. Since any object whether it be an electron, atom, or elephant requires a continual flow of information back and forth within itself, we would never expect to encounter an extended object traveling at a speed greater than that of light relative to us. If the object were moving faster, those processes which hold it together could not function and hence it could not exist in our reality. The electrical waves moving from one atom to another would be left behind, just as the waves produced by a jet aircraft are left behind when it travels faster than sound.

A group of dolphins swimming through the dark ocean keeps together by the clicks and whistles its members make. Were the dolphins to swim faster than the speed of sound in water, they could not keep together.

Likewise, were we to move faster than the speed of light

as seen by someone else, our atoms would appear to disperse and in his viewpoint we would fall apart. We could not exist in the world of that observer.

Similarly, one edge of a cube must be in communication with all adjacent edges in order for the cube to be an authentic cube. Since that communication can travel no faster than the speed of light, the faster the cube moves with respect to us, the longer it takes the signal to propagate from edge to edge. Consequently the fast-moving cube should be distorted. The difference is more than mere optical illusion. By all the techniques we have available to us to investigate the nature of the fast cube, it would appear distorted. Since a normally rigid object, a cube built of steel, for instance, must change shape freely with changes in velocity, our old ideas of rigidity and permanence of form are placed in serious jeopardy by this simple idea of a speed limit to communication.

Even more disruptive to our notions of reality is the recognition that it is impossible to describe the entirety of an object at one time. Because of the finite speed of light no object has an instantaneous existence. All extended objects are fuzzy time averages. In order for an object to be totally present at a given instant of time, instantaneous communication would be required. Since that is impossible, all parts of an object exist in the past of every other part. Our present does not exist. One not only needs a clairvoyant to foretell the future but also to foretell the present. For us, the viewers, a cube lies in our past with different parts of it extending to different distances into the past.

The single, isolated object upon which Newton built his world cannot exist in our newer view. Nothing larger than a mathematical point can exist as a single event. Instead, we have to describe objects and things in terms of *processes*. A chair is not an object but a process upon which a human process can sit while reading that process which we call a book.

In order to explore further what we mean by process, let

us consider the space-time diagram on which time is plotted vertically and one dimension of space is plotted horizontally (see Figure 1). Events such as birth and death of individuals can be located as specific points on such a diagram. A "world line" connecting these two points can describe the life of a man.

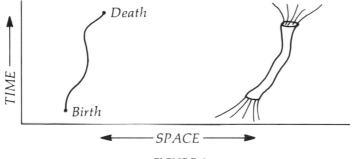

FIGURE 1.

Whenever the world line is used to represent the motion of matter through space and time, its inclination relative to the time-axis must correspond to speeds less than that of light. A vertical line represents zero relative velocity. The horizontal line represents an infinite speed and therefore cannot represent anything in the real world. Since there can be no horizontal structures in the space-time diagram, the lines themselves must have zero width. Every object therefore must consist of a bundle of infinitesimally narrow world lines; that bundle we call a "world tube."

Only if we humans could reduce ourselves in size to mathematical points, could we be described on such a diagram as a series of individual point-events on a one dimensional line. "I" as a point could meet "you" at a particular point in time and space. Since we would both be points, we could exist together, instantaneously at one point on the space-time diagram.

But since we are large and spill out into a relatively large volume of space, we are more like ill-defined smears made by an inky worm crawling across a piece of paper.

Our own individual world tubes contain countless smaller tubes corresponding to the movement of matter and energy through us. Those tubes in turn contain even smaller ones within them. We are bundles of hairy tubes intertwining like eels with other tubes, portions of a hierarchy of tubes extending up and down in scale to the edges of our reality.

Since each world tube consists of smaller tubes which have entered it from a wider field of space-time, it is impossible to separate it from that field in which it is embedded. A plant grows, drawing into itself radiant energy from the sun, hydrogen from the beginning of the universe, carbon from a supernova, water from a nearby spring. The world lines of all these processes co-mingle briefly in the world tube of the plant, and then when it dies they disperse and scatter through space-time. The world tube of a piece of granite exists for a longer period of time than the world tube of a bacteria. The tube of a rock is smooth as it interchanges little energy or matter with its surroundings. Living systems are tubes with hair corresponding to the energy and matter that flows into and out of them during their lives.

That which we used to view as an isolated object is no more. And a person of the twentieth century is now a pattern of tubes with long tendrils reaching far into space and time. There is no break between the person and the surrounding field, no boundary where at one side there is a person and at the other side there is no person. Into and out of a person flows the universe.

Again we recognize that the old Newtonian view of the separability of the world into islands is no longer valid. Our reality has become an uninterrupted flow, and we find ourselves back again in that deeply running river of Heraclites. We are experiencing a world which is composed of a complex hierarchy of smaller and larger patterns of flow.

The so-called "things" of the world are thus features of the flow like candle flames and water cascades where flow lines converge and then diverge. These patterns are assembled into a hierarchy of larger and less stable patterns. Many electron and proton patterns join into the pattern of the chemical molecule. Those patterns of flow join into living cells, then people, and into nations, gathering together for a few decades as fragile patterns and then dissolving back into the surrounding field.

3. The Field Versus the Particle

The tolling bell
Measures time but not our time, rung by the unhurried
Ground swell.

T.S. Eliot "The Dry Salvages"

Our world is filled with processes not things, and these processes are all interconnected by a network of world lines. The atomism which started with the Greeks and which was carried to triumph by Newton and the Industrial Revolution has been replaced by a world tapestry in which particles and people are merely regions in which there are higher concentrations of world lines.

The description of that changing world tapestry is our new geometry, a geometry we must experience from the inside rather than view from a distance. As matter moves through it the structure of space-time changes like an ocean which lifts and falls with the changing pull of the moon. In the vicinity of matter space-time is positively curved as a sphere is positively curved. As matter changes location, space-time flows from one shape into another. If matter is removed, space-time becomes less curved; were all matter absent, space-time would be flat.

Flat space is Euclid's space; flat space is the medium in which Newton's force of gravity is valid; and flat space is empty space. As a test of his equations of General Relativity Einstein investigated the characteristics of a universe devoid of matter and energy and found that only in such a meaningless approximation to our universe would his equations reduce to those of Newtonian gravity. The physics of Newton has been crowned by success piled upon success during the past 300 years; yet his physics is no more than an approximation of the theory of Einstein for an empty universe.

Although the theory of Newton can be obtained from the more general theory of Einstein, the two theories are as different as light and dark. Even though they reach roughly similar conclusions about the behavior of gravity near the earth, they proceed from mutually exclusive views of the world. One assumes instantaneous action-at-a-distance across empty space in a universe in which discrete objects are the basic building blocks. The other coming 250 years later disallows discreteness and strives to describe the universe as a continuum in which interactions propagate at a finite speed across the field of space-time.

Is one view any better than the other? If they were equally successful, we would certainly choose the simplest of these opposing models. Were the General Theory of Relativity no more than an elegant way of deriving the equations of Newton, we should dismiss it as a bit of arrogant elitism. But, it turns out that the General Theory does make three predictions which differ from those made by the Newtonian theory. Therein lies the possibility of testing and choosing between these two alternatives.

The first of the three predictions of General Relativity concerns the deflection of a beam of light as it passes through the gravitational field of a massive object. The Einstein theory predicts that at the edge of the sun the light of another star should be deflected by an angle of 1.75 seconds of arc while the Newtonian theory predicts a deflection half that amount (see Figure 2). The first measurement of this effect was made by the English astronomers Eddington and Dyson, May 29, 1919 during a total eclipse of the sun. The results appeared to be in beautiful agreement with Einstein's prediction and clearly disagreed with the predictions of Newtonian theory. It was a fine touch of irony that the theory of a German should have been successfully tested by

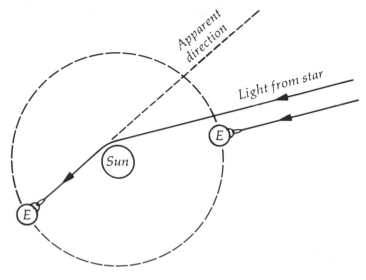

FIGURE 2.

Englishmen so soon after the First World War, especially when the theory was to replace one created by an Englishman some 250 years earlier.

A second prediction of the Einstein theory is that light escaping from a gravitational object should be shifted to the red end of the spectrum. Even for light it is a struggle escaping from a star. It uses up energy, as though climbing up stairs out of the basement, and lower energy photons are redder photons. The Newtonian theory predicted no such shift in color. Light from the sun should be shifted to the red by two parts per million according to General Relativity. Recent measurements confirm that prediction. Much larger red shifts associated with dense white dwarf stars like the companion to Sirius, Sirius B have been predicted and confirmed. The most precise test for this effect was performed in the laboratory by Pound and Rebka in 1960. This experiment has verified Einstein's prediction with an accuracy of one per cent. Again Einstein wins, Newton loses.

Finally, the Einstein theory predicts a systematic change in the orbit of a planet as it moves around the sun. Due to

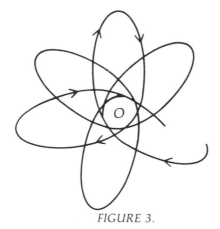

FIGURE 3.

the curvature of space near the sun each successive orbit should advance slightly, and after many centuries the planet will have traced out a rosette-like figure (see Figure 3).

In contrast, the Newtonian theory predicts that a single planet circling the sun will exactly repeat its orbit each time around. The presence of other planets will cause the orbit to advance, but in the case of the planet Mercury, the advance predicted by Newtonian theory is too small by forty-three seconds of arc per century compared to the observed rate of advance.

There is a touch of irony to the fact that the seeds for this challenge to Newtonian physics were planted by the Frenchman Leverrier who had succeeded in accrediting the Newtonian theory by his successful prediction of the position of Neptune. Leverrier also had observed that the advance of the orbit of Mercury was occurring 35 seconds of arc per century faster than it should according to Newtonian theory, and he suggested that this excess could be produced by a small planet lying between Mercury and the sun. The postulated planet was named Vulcan which in subsequent years has acquired a certain notoriety as the home of Mr. Spock of "Star Trek" fame. However, Leverrier's success with Neptune was not to be repeated. Searches during numerous total eclipses failed to reveal the presence of Vulcan and Newtonian gravity appeared to be in trouble. By 1882, the discrepancy between theory and observation became more firmly established as a more precise value of 43 seconds per century was determined. Some 30 years later Einstein showed that one of the predictions of his general theory was that Mercury's orbit should advance by 43 seconds of arc per century.

One cannot emphasize too strongly the significance of these triumphs of Einstein over that of Newton. It was more than a struggle between one mathematical equation and another; the issue was between a continuous universe and a discrete universe. The verdict was returned in favor of the wholeness of the world.

Einstein was seeking to couple the behavior of the microcosm to that of the macrocosm. The planet which orbits the sun is not behaving as an isolated object acted upon merely by the sun, but is moving through a field of curved space-time, the detailed structure of which is determined by the distribution of all the matter in the universe. As that matter moves and changes, so changes the structure of space-time. Since our physics is supported by the gently curving ocean of space-time it is possible that even the laws of physics are coupled to the large scale structure of the universe; as the universe changes through expansion, so perhaps will our local physics. Now we enter a very speculative realm of modern physics.

If there is a coupling between local and cosmic events, it would seem reasonable for the strength of that coupling to change as the universe expands. Exactly how that should occur is not immediately clear, but it is possible that it might be detected in changing ratios of physical constants. The first hint of such a change was discovered by P. A. M. Dirac in 1937 when he noticed that the ratio of the electrical force to the gravitational force is approximately equal to 10^{40} which is also approximately the age of the universe in jiffies. A jiffy is the time required for light to cross a proton.

The radius of the universe divided by the radius of the proton is also approximately 10^{40}.

Since, quite obviously, the age and size of the universe are changing, it is a strange coincidence that they should be equal to the ratio of the electrical to the gravitational force at just the time when mankind is first able to make such comparisons. Is it purely coincidence or perhaps could it be that the ratio of these two fundamental forces of nature is also changing with time? Sensing that such a coincidence might be the hint of an unrevealed "truth," Dirac proposed that the constant of gravity, G, changes with time in such a manner to make the ratio of the two forces always approximately equal to the age of the universe in jiffies.

If G becomes smaller while the universe grows older, then the Dirac ratio can be understood as something more than mere coincidence. A constant, a fundamental constant, one of those things upon which the apparent stability of our world has been based, has thus been challenged: no longer immutable but perhaps a changling like the rest of us.

So far the Dirac theory is only conjecture. The best opportunity for measuring a change in G comes from analysis of radar observations of Mercury and Venus. As the constant of gravity changes, both the period and the distance of the planet in its orbit around the sun should change. A comparison of the orbital periods of Mercury and Venus with an atomic clock (which does not depend upon G) establishes an upper limit on the variation of G which is close to that of the theory of Dirac. It is expected that within a few years there should be a definitive test of the theory of Dirac.

The consequences of even a slight variation in G are astonishing. If G was larger in the past and gravity was consequently stronger, stars would have been brighter than we usually suppose them to have been. For instance, at the time when the solar system was forming, some 4.5 billion years ago, the sun would have been brighter by a factor of three due to the larger value of G. The temperature of the earth would have been close to the boiling point of water.

As G decreased throughout the universe, the temperature of the earth would have slowly fallen to its present value of 23° Centigrade.

The earliest known life forms are bacteria and the astronomer Fred Hoyle proposes that it is no mere coincidence that these simple creatures are extremely heat resistant. Some bacteria are able to survive in temperatures near 95° C in the hot springs of Yellowstone National Park. Perhaps, Hoyle suggests, the entire sweep of biological evolution on the earth has been dictated by the expansion of the universe. Not just a spaceship-earth but an incubator-earth, our planet may have slowly cooled in resonance to the changing value of the gravitational constant. At first the warm oceans were necessary in order that chemical reactions occur sufficiently rapidly to form biological molecules; but at those temperatures only the simplest of biological systems could have survived. As the temperature of the early earth fell, life may have moved outward from its simple beginnings to increasingly complex forms at a rate established by the movement of distant galaxies.

When the temperature dropped to 75° C from the near boiling temperature at which bacteria can survive, blue-green algae could begin to thrive. Sometime later when the temperature fell to 55–60° C, fungi could exist. Eventually when the oceans reached a temperature of 45–50° C, protozoa began to swarm.

It may thus have taken intelligent life some two billion years to evolve on the earth not because of the slowness of the processes of mutation and natural selection, but because complex life could not have survived in a universe with a larger value of G.

The changing gravitational constant may have geological consequences also, for the earth may be ripping itself apart as G decreases. The interior of the earth is compressed by the weight of the outer layers. A decrease in G would mean that the weight of the overlying layers should be getting less and the earth should therefore be expanding. The radius of the earth should be increasing at the rate of between 6 and 10 kilometers per 100 million years if G varies inversely with the age of the universe, as in the Dirac theory. The earth's crust must crack to allow new material to emerge from below. If G varies inversely with the age of the universe as Dirac has proposed, the surface area of the earth may be increasing by about a million square kilometers each 100 million years. The great rifts in the ocean basins, the drift of continents, the raising up of mountain ranges, and even the devastating earthquakes may be the result of the earth's response to the expansion of the universe.

A related coupling between the universe and the local world involves what is known as Mach's principle, named after the Austrian philosopher-scientist who contributed much to Einstein's philosophy. Mach's idea was that the inertia of an object does not originate in that object itself, but results from its reluctance to accelerate relative to the stars and galaxies of the universe. If one is running down a street pushing a baby-buggy and hits a curb, the baby flies out because of his inertia. According to the Machian interpretation, the flying baby is resisting acceleration relative to the distant galaxies of the universe. In other words the baby is better coupled to the galaxies than to its own buggy. That coupling may be accomplished by the interaction between the baby and a field of matter which has been generated by those galaxies. The inertial mass of each particle in the universe may thus originate in the interaction with this field.

UNIVERSE OF GALAXIES → MATTER FIELD → PARTICLE MASS

As the mass content of the universe changes, so should the inertia of individual particles change. Thus if one were to remove, one by one, the galaxies which surround us in the universe, we would find that the inertia of ourselves and the things which surround us would all decrease. Buggy belts would be less necessary for babies in a universe with fewer galaxies. The inertia of an object would vanish, in the Machian viewpoint, when the matter in the universe vanished. One solitary particle would have no inertial mass.

Common to all that I have discussed in this chapter is the concept of an ever-present and inter-penetrating field which generates perhaps all of the attributes of physical matter. The individual object has lost its absolute identity and has become dependent upon the larger world of space-time, such that when that larger world changes so changes the character of the objects floating within it.

4. The Hall of Mirrors

The dance along the artery
The circulation of the lymph
Are figures in the drift of stars.
T. S. Eliot, "Burnt Norton"

Not just a stage upon which to act or a container in which to live, but a lover with infinitely many ways to please, the universe is inexhaustible in her variety. The number and variety of surprises which mankind has encountered during the last few decades are astonishing: electrons behaving like waves; crumpled space-time in the form of black holes; quasars varying in brightness by amounts equal to hundreds of galaxies; exploding galaxies scattering plumes of stars; spinning neutron stars with fragile and fracturing crusts. The list could go on and on for there seems to be no end to this occurring of the unanticipated.

With remarkable ingenuity nature does not repeat the same pattern at different levels of scale. The old dictum "as above, so below" is neither very exact nor is it useful. No matter how similar the atom and the solar system appear in caricature, they are not identical. The electron is an entirely different creature from a planet, and an analogy serves only to confuse.

We are not living in a building with a monotonous repetition of phenomena at each floor. The exploration of our home is not like that of an elevator ride which carries us past identical floor after identical floor, each with the same floor plan, with the same square area, with the same kinds of people doing the same kinds of tasks. The floors are related and mutually dependent, but they are not alike either in quantity or in quality.

The physicist David Bohm has proposed the concept of qualitative infinity to express the unlimited variety of basically different phenomena which our universe seems to possess. He suggests that the experiences of experimental and observational science during the last century can not justify any a priori restrictions on the conditions and properties that may exist in nature: "nature may have in it an infinity of potentially or actually significant qualities." The promise of unlimited qualities is far more exciting than merely unlimited quantities. There are an infinite quantity of ways of arranging the grains of sand in a sandbox, but it always has one quality, that of being a sandbox. Only when children are in the sandbox interacting with the sand, does it acquire new qualities.

The richness of the world comes in part from the number of interconnections which can exist between different phenomena. The continuous-field concept of modern physics implies that every object regardless of its location in the hierarchy of sizes in the universe is dependent for its existence upon a system of roots which extend through the field which enfolds it. Since the nature of the field must be influenced by the objects themselves, there must be a strong reciprocal relationship between objects and the field. Each thing which exists in nature must make some contribution to the whole field of the universe and as that thing changes, grows, or dies so should the whole universe undergo a related transformation. Each object is a representative of the universe with which it is in contact, and as that universe changes so too should the object change. As we have seen, the expansion of the universe may change the gravitational constant and the inertial masses of individual particles. The removal, one by one, of those particles may alter the background field such that the inertial masses of the remaining particles are lessened.

Because of this phenomenon of reciprocity the world is always changing. We do not just peer at the world as if it were a remote and distant planet shimmering in a tele-scope, but rather we actively influence our reality as it influences us. As R. D. Laing has described relationships between people, so can we describe ours with the world: we experience ourselves as experienced by the world experiencing itself as experienced by us. The restlessness of the world means that the fruits of reciprocity will always be different. There should be no limit to the new kinds of phenomena that can occur and no limit to the physical laws which may be used to describe them. Qualitative infinity thus implies an infinity of physics.

In the literature of Hwa Yen Buddhism there is a description of how reality must appear to a Buddha which is intriguing in its similarity to these assertions that change, reciprocity, and wholeness are fundamental attributes of our world. The teachings of this school of Buddhism are largely based upon the *Garland Sutra* which has as its primary goal the revealing of the Buddha realm of infinity. The glimpse we get of Buddha's view of the universe is of an intricately interrelated cosmos which contains an infinity of "interpenetrating, simultaneously arising, and mutually containing realms."

As it is used in the *Garland Sutra,* a realm is meant to be a collection of related activities, processes, and thoughts. For an example of such a realm, let us use the many-faced sun. Co-existing in that orange ball of sunrise and sunset (in a simple yet almost mysterious way) are numerous identifiable realms living harmoniously together. For many the return of the sun in the spring means a growth of crops; for others the sun can mean drought and death. The sun is the god Ra which rules the heavens and which sleeps in the waters of the night. For the modern sun worshipper it is a source of tan or burn, and flashing diamonds on the rippling surface of water. The sun is the place of emergence of life, the inexhaustible grail, the on-going nourisher and re-creator of mankind. For an astronomer the sun is a ball containing 10^{57} protons with a central temperature of 15 million degrees; in its core hydrogen atoms are fusing together to form helium. That these different realms can co-exist with each other in that single object is referred to by the authors of the *Garland Sutra* as this quality of being interpenetrating and simultaneously arising.

Whether it be a tree, a glass of water, or the entire cosmos, each involves an infinitude of interpenetrating realms. These various realms may be ordered in a number of ways. They may be arranged in a hierarchy of sizes, such as galaxies which contain solar systems which contain atoms. Perhaps there is no limit to the number or sizes of these realms. We cannot see beyond the horizon of our universe, which lies some 10 or 15 billion light years in the distance, nor can we imagine the presence of structures smaller than the Planck length of 10^{-33} cm. But these are our present boundaries and we know better than to say they are absolute. Perhaps through the doorways of black holes lie larger and smaller realms.

The authors of the *Garland Sutra* go beyond merely noting the possibility of such an infinity of realms piled one on top of another. The next step is indeed a difficult one: in the perception of a Buddha, this hierarchy of sizes can be turned inside out. The small atom contains not only an infinite sequence of smaller realms, but it also contains within it all of the larger universe. Such an extraordinary notion is described as the non-obstruction of mutual consent. Not only do the events of the universe depend upon each other but they contain one another in the sense that there is a reciprocity and inter-immanence between all things. Everything can be seen to be at once both an image and a reflector of everything else.

Alfred North Whitehead describes this notion in terms of mutual immanence: ". . . the togetherness of things involves some doctrine of mutual immanence. In some sense or other, this community of the actualities of the world means each happening is a factor in the nature of every other happening. . . . We are in the world and the world is in us.''

What an awesome new dimension has been added to our reality: each and every object in the universe is at once a mirror and an image. It is a mirror because it reflects all things and it is an image because it is simultaneously reflected by all other things. Thus, to the extent that one thing is related to all other things, it reflects them all; and to the extent that the existence of any particular thing must depend on other things, it is a reflection of objects other than itself.

There is a sense of such simultaneous containment and reflection of infinite realms in Mach's principle in which the mass of an electron reflects the distribution of masses of galaxies at the edge of the universe. The whole of the universe is, for instance, mirrored in the electron which itself is a changing image of that universe.

Garma D. Chang in his book on Hwa Yen Buddhism, *The Buddhist Teaching of Totality*, relates a parable about containment and reflection:

> A monk is preaching the Dharma to his disciple in a room where hangs a mirror. . . . The mirror reflects a picture of two individuals facing each other; one is preaching and the other is listening. To describe the interrelationship of the participants of this phenomenon, we can either say that the monk within the mirror of the disciple is preaching the Dharma to the disciple within the mirror of the monk, or we can say that the disciple within the mirror of the monk is listening to the Dharma preached by the monk within the mirror of the disciple. When Buddha preaches the Dharma to man it is not a two-way relationship—one preaches and the other listens, but a four-way relationship. The Buddha who is within man's mind preaches the Dharma to

man who is within Buddha's mind, and the man who is within Buddha's mind listens to the preaching of the Buddha who is within man's mind.

Let us briefly experiment with this parable using a man, an electron, and the universe. The electron and man are not just mirrors reflecting the whole cosmos, but each is a region of the cosmic field reflecting itself. Since each region of the field contains the totality of the field within itself, we can say that everything reflects everything else. A very short version of the parable might go something like this: The universe is changed by a man who is contained by the universe and who contains within himself the entire universe when he asks a question of an electron which is contained by both the universe and man, and which contains within itself both the universe and man.

As with all of our encounters with infinity we feel giddy. The world is open, not closed, and that openness is always a little unsettling. The possibilities of extracting new things from the changing universe are unlimited. The river changes as we step into it because the river, which is within us and which is us, changes as we change.

5. The King Must Die

.

In my end is my beginning.
T. S. Eliot, "East Coker"

Death is part of that cycle of which rebirth is the other half. It is an act of transformation from one stage to another. The ancient tradition of killing the old god-king was a ritual reenactment of the cycle which must not be allowed to stop cycling. The king must die for the good of the people to prevent death of the world by stagnation.

Once each twelve years the king in the south Indian province of Quilacare had to sacrifice himself. His death was timed to be in rhythm with the movement of Jupiter along its orbit; when Jupiter would begin its retrograde motion in the sky, the king would climb a wooden scaffolding covered with silk hangings. Then in full view of his people, he took sharp knives and proceeded to cut off parts of his body, nose, ears, lips, and as much of his flesh as he was able, throwing them among the people. When so much of his blood was spilt that he began to faint, he slit his throat.

Another example of regicide comes from the Sudan where among the Shilluk the ritual murder of the king took place every seven years, or more often if the crops failed or the cattle began dying before his seventh year reign was finished. When the time of his death arrived as determined precisely by the priests who knew the will of god, it was performed by the chief noble on a dark night near the new moon, after the first seeds had been placed in the ground. The king was strangled in silence so that none of the tribe should know of it. He was buried with a living virgin at his side. When the two bodies had rotted, the bones were gathered into the skin of a bull. A year later the new king was named, and on the old king's grave, cattle were speared to death by the hundred.

The dying king placed himself in phase with the rhythm of the world, for the forfeiture of his life and the dismemberment of his body were necessary to keep alive the supreme mystery of the cycling earth. The earth which becomes gray and tired must be discarded and replaced with a new one in the spring. To insure that change never ceases, the king must perform sympathetic magic.

In a similar fashion science must pass through these cycles of death and re-birth. The uncovering of new facts and the subsequent interpretation of those facts are the two faces of our science. Interpretation essentially means interrelation. New facts must be tied to the old facts. They must be reconciled with the existing collection of data, and in that reconcilation they acquire meaning as we see where they fit into the "scheme of things." Since that scheme may work for some facts and not for others it must be changed periodically through a scientific revolution.

During the era when a particular scientific myth is working, the effort of all the scientists is directed toward bringing the whole of the world into consistency with the existing models. Chaos is replaced by order and confusion by understanding. During this phase, science develops in a cumulative and organic manner as more and more of the sensory experiences of the world are reconciled with each other. The scientific journals bulge with newly written research papers and the world becomes familiar and comfortable. At every turn it is like meeting an old friend, slightly changed perhaps as one performs new experiments, but basically the same old bloke. The variety and diversity become distilled into a few simple concepts and he who knows those concepts is seemingly invested with great power.

But, when a scientific revolution occurs, the old myth is killed and replaced by one that is fully and completely new. The old facts remain but the relation between facts has changed. A new science is invented because the old is no longer fruitful, no longer able to make accurate predictions. Only if the old and new are logically incompatible can there be any improvement: not built upon the old, not merely a refinement of the old, but something fully new?

Revolutions do not happen very often in science. There are too many self-maintaining safeguards built into science to invite frequent change. But when it does happen the new science is not like a bud on an old cactus. The old plant is cut down entirely, turned into mulch, and although the same ground remains, an entirely new plant emerges.

In the fifteenth century, the planets were not in the correct places according to the Ptolemaic theory, nor did they vary in size or brightness in the right way. These problems could not be satisfactorily eliminated by modifying the old theory; it had been patched too often already. These anomalies could be resolved only by a totally new viewpoint. Only by bodily picking up the earth, kicking and screaming, moving it away from the center of the solar system and by putting the sun in its place could order be returned to the heavens.

The phases of Venus, the changes in the apparent sizes of the planets, the orbits of the planets derived from careful observation, are all fully at odds with the Ptolemaic epicyclic theory. Neither in its basic physics or philosophy did the sun-centered cosmology grow out of the earth-centered view. There was a jump at the time of the Copernican revolution to a new structure and the old one died.

The earth is not at the center of the solar system. The planets do not follow circular epicycles. The Ptolemaic theory is basically and fundamentally wrong, basically and fundamentally different from the sun-centered cosmology. There was not a smooth, continuous transition to the new "administration"; they spoke different languages, shared different philosophies, emphasized different items, measured "truth" in different ways.

Likewise, as we have already argued, the physics of Einstein and the physics of Newton are fundamentally incompatible. Einstein's theory can be accepted only with the understanding that Newton's theory was wrong; the birth of a new theory implies the death of the old. The appearance of the Theory of Relativity involved a shift from a particulate to a continuous world. Although Newtonian dynamics is still used with great success by most engineers and in selected situations by many physicists, basic concepts such as mass and force have entirely different definitions in the two systems. Newtonian mass is conserved and absolute. In Einstein's model mass is exchangeable with energy. Only at low velocities do the kinds of masses have the same value, but even then they do not have the same meaning.

Our reality is not equivalent to the external world, nor is it a copy of that world, but rather it is a highly evolved construction which is ever subject to change. As Bronowski has commented: "Our experiences do not merely link us to the outside world; they are us and they are the world for us; they make us part of the world. We get a false picture of the world if we regard it as a set of events that have their own absolute sequence and that we merely watch." We make our world because the full world out there (whatever that means) is not available to us; nor even do we have time enough to explore that which is available before we are forced to make decisions. We have developed categories and filtering techniques which are aimed primarily at individual biological survival. The agility to perceive and manipulate discrete objects has significant survival value for humans. Our perceptions are directed toward discrete on/off objects which stand out against the background. The detection of moving predictors is a more valuable ability than the perception of subtleties in a background. Our consciousness usually filters out slowly varying aspects of the background and retains only survival related stimuli.

An important role of our sensory system is to discard irrelevant information. Were we to permit everything to enter our awareness, we would be overwhelmed by the mass of "useless" and "irrelevant" information: all would be a "blooming, buzzing confusion," in the words of William James. Take the frog, for instance, as a well-studied example of sensory filtering. According to the researches of Lettvin and colleagues at the Massachusetts Institute of Technology, only four different kinds of messages are transmitted from its eye to its brain. Although capable of perceiving a variety of complex images, the eye of the frog is connected to its brain in such a manner that only certain types of messages are sent. The frog's eye has evolved to discard useless information, and concentrates on visual stimulae associated with the approach of a bird of prey or an edible bug.

Our own categories act as short cuts for experience, just as a large body of experience may be evoked by a subset of that experience. A particular experience "makes sense" if it can be related to the category. It is then familiar and we do not need to treat it as a new experience. Since a single experience can stimulate a constellation of related experiences, the techniques enable us to deal with the world of sensory experiences more rapidly than if we had to treat each experience as new and isolated.

The danger is that we may misinterpret the category; the wrong set of experiences may be evoked, or we may not experience it at all if it does not correspond to our categories. Since this reality of ours with its many categories is something we have constructed ourselves in order to survive on this particular planet, it must be just one of many possible alternate realities.

The psychologist Ames suggests that our accepted reality is a transaction between the perceiver and the external world. In spite of the great flow of information reaching us, it is not sufficient to provide the full story. Based upon our prior experience and upon the categories we have created, we "bet" that a particular aspect of the external world has a certain form and meaning. As we acquire more information that bet undergoes continuous correction.

We are not extracting meaning from the world but adding to it by trying out these trial balloons. These bets or categories last only so long as they do not contradict the physical phenomena we encounter. But until that time when we realize something is wrong with our categories, our world consists of these personal constructions.

Most of our world is imprinted upon us by our culture, especially the culture we learn as children. It is unsettling to consider how much potential richness may be denied us by excessive filtering through categories we were given as children.

The extraordinary limiting ability of these categories is dramatized by recent experiments at Cambridge University on kittens which were reared in visual environments consisting only of vertical stripes or horizontal stripes. When the kittens emerged from their striped nurseries, they behaved in ways that corresponded closely with the orientation of the stripes they were used to experiencing.

Horizontal kittens were capable of jumping into a chair, but when walking on the floor they were always bumping into chair legs as if the legs were invisible to them. The horizontal animals were blind to vertical structures; they had no vertical feature detectors, so they could not see anything composed of vertical lines. The vertical kittens had no problem avoiding vertical obstructions, but they never tried to jump into a chair; it was as if the horizontal chair seat did not exist.

These kittens had a limited set of very restrictive categories. Ours are less restrictive; at least, that is our faith. And we hope that we are capable of one or two switches of our categories in a lifetime.

The switch from one set of human categories to another generally occurs at great speed. It occurs when the person involved is prepared for the major restructuring. The process is like the sudden crystallization which occurs when a seed crystal is dropped into a supersaturated solution. The Russian Revolution shook the world in ten days and the

United States Constitution was written in a few weeks. Learning to ski or ride a bicycle are examples of sudden restructuring of skills.

These jumps in restructuring are frequently associated with a crisis involving the old categories. The old models will not work; newly acquired data does not fit the predictions. Psychologists speak of cognitive dissonance which precedes a personality restructuring and which may be manifest as anxiety, anger, aggression or withdrawal. When the new pattern becomes available, there is a great sense of relief as reconciliation occurs between the model and the world. These restructuring experiences generally move in the direction of simplification. The many details of the world, once bewildering in their multitude, can be seen in perspective, unified by a new way of seeing. In the words of Jung: "It is not that something different is seen, but that one sees differently." The wandering stars, the swinging moon, the falling apple could suddenly be taken in all at once through the simplification of Newtonian gravity. Now they, and much more, can be combined through the vision of the curvature of space-time provided by Einstein.

An extremely interesting aspect of these death-birth experiences is that there is often a leap over the current structure. A jump is made across the established categories from the old to the new. The reason for this jump appears to be the self-maintaining ability of any successful structure. Problems can rarely be solved on the level of problems, for in any self-stablizing situation, any build-up of conflicting processes usually evokes a counter-balancing response. As we have already noted, no simple modification of Newtonian mechanics could lead either to relativity. It was not a simple matter of marching in an orderly manner onward from Newton to Einstein. There is always considerable reluctance on the part of scientists to engage in major revisions in the structure of their science, for too much is invested in one particularly approach. Moreover, since the science of the day generally is one which is able to account successfully for almost all of the details of the world, the first response to the discovery of an anomalous result is to attempt to modify the current models, preserving as much as possible of their essential strengths.

Thus the epicycles of the Greeks were progressively altered to fit the newer more precise observations as they became available. Before the Copernican revolution, the whole of astronomy was involved in making ever more elaborate adjustments to the epicycle theory. When he was introduced to the very contrived state of Ptolemaic astronomy, Alphonso X of Castile remarked: "If the Lord Almighty had consulted me before embarking upon the Creation I should have recommended something simpler." The awkwardness and complexity of the system which Copernicus killed resulted from the self-maintaining forces present in the body of astronomy at that time.

A true revolutionary was needed, one who could do more than make minor modifications. In a sense Copernicus descended to an earlier scheme, the two-thousand-year-old heliocentric model of Aristarchus, and then vaulted over the deeply-entrenched Ptolemaic astronomy to establish his new structure of the cosmos.

One sees this phenomenon of level jumping in the rather curious connection between the sub-rational and the super-rational. Intuition, sudden flashes of insight, and even mystical experiences seem to play a role in the restructuring of science. In a sense, these are all subrational experiences which are sometimes much more effective than a protracted struggle with a problem on the rational level. Eliot describes this technique of level jumping in "East Coker":

> In order to arrive at what you do not know
>> You must go by a way which is the way of ignorance.
> In order to possess what you do not possess
>> You must go by the way of dispossession.
> In order to arrive at what you are not
>> You must go through the way in which you are not.

These excursions which take man out of his level are uniquely human experiences. They are examples of the strange and inscrutable process of creative individualism whereby through the process of induction new order is given to the assembled facts.

No programmed computer can accomplish this level jumping since the computer always operates on the level of its builders. The men who are able to make the leap are frequently either very young or are new to a field and are thereby able to avoid being bound by a fondness for the established mode.

Man, irrational in part, swayed by the primordial elements of his nervous system, lies at the intersection of the worlds, between the new and the old. He is needed to play that vital role of killing the old and recreating the new. Without him the world, condemned to the same old tired patterns, would drown in tradition and inaction.

6. The Photon Eaters

O dark dark dark. They all go into the dark,
The vacant interstellar spaces, the vacant into the vacant.
T. S. Eliot, "East Coker"

Time and change: what obvious partners but such elusive quarry. How man has struggled with the concept of time! It cannot be placed etherized on a table or captured squirming on a pin to be studied at one's leisure.

"What, then, is time? If no one asks me, I know what it is. If I wish to explain it to him who asks me, I do not know," agonized St. Augustine in his *Confessions.*

There is a delicious paradox to the presence of a human philosopher wrestling with the problem of time. The philosopher is challenged by such an abstract puzzle because he is a complex mixture of atoms. The solitary hydrogen atom from which he arose does not ask such questions. During the last 4.5 billion years atoms have clustered together to produce mankind in a process of synthesis which runs opposite to the steady disintegration taking place in the universe beyond the earth. With disintegration so universal, the philosopher has little or no business even living in this universe, let alone asking bothersome questions about time.

Man seems to be swimming upstream against the current, against the flow of time in that river of Heraclites. We humans are unlikely parasites living off a disintegrating star which is gradually converting its order into disorder as it scatters energy in all directions. Our earth like an ingenious green leaf which is able to reach out and grab some of the original order, soaks up an infinitesimal fraction of that sunlight and converts it into other forms of energy.

The growth of disorder in the universe is the result of a flow from the improbable to the probable, from the highly concentrated fireball of creation to the thin and tepid broth in which we are now floating. This spontaneous change of state from order to disorder is a well-known phenomenon on the earth. Every mother is only too familiar with it as she watches her home become increasingly disorganized; dust settles on the tables, windows become fly-specked, and newspapers become scattered. Like the tidy home, a small bottle of gas held at high pressure is also improbable. When the stopper is pulled the atoms scatter through the room like galaxies in an expanding universe, and the likely overtakes the unlikely. Never in the experience of mankind has the reverse process occurred spontaneously. If only the crumbs would fly back onto the toast or the scattered toys leap back into the toy box, the housewife sighs.

Such irreversibility of crumbs and toast applies only to situations which have different likelihoods of coming into being. Crumbs are always more likely than toast, whereas heads and tails are equally likely when a single coin is tossed on a table. However, when two coins are used, then the irreversibility of events begins to become noticeable. It is twice as likely that two coins will land as one head and one tail than as either two heads or two tails for the reason that there are twice as many ways to generate the head-tail combination than the other two combinations. Thus coins starting out as two heads or two tails when shaken should more often become head-tail combinations; the reverse sequence is unlikely. With more coins, the sequence going from equal numbers of heads and tails to all of one kind is even less likely. With enough coins, it becomes as unlikely as the spontaneous generation of a tidy room. Since there are always many more ways to produce disorder than order, the disordered condition is the more likely one in our universe, and it is therefore in the direction of increasing disorder that we spontaneously move. Such movement is the essence of the second law of thermodynamics: *For an isolated system the direction of spontaneous change is from order to disorder.*

As it is frequently presented, the second law of thermodynamics uses the concept of entropy, which is simply a measure of the complexity and probability of a system. High complexity corresponds to low probability and low entropy. A large crystal of salt has more order and thus less entropy than an equal weight of small crystals. A pile of dust has more entropy than a statue; pots of paint have more entropy than a painting. One hundred and fifty pounds of isolated atoms of hydrogen, carbon, oxygen, and nitrogen have more entropy, i. e. less complex organization, than a person of the same weight. In terms of entropy, the second law may be stated as follows: *The entropy of an isolated system increases or remains constant. Entropy does not spontaneously decrease.*

As most parents know only too well, the child's room varies between states of maximum and minimum entropy. When the toys are scattered at random across the floor, the room is close to a state of maximum entropy. When it is cleaned by a parent, and the toys are stored in a toy box, its entropy has been minimized. A band of children upon entering the room can quickly and with no effort at all return the room to its state of maximum entropy.

Although we, child and adult alike, create entropy, we are clearly low entropy systems ourselves. Complicated and highly organized biochemical systems, human creatures are the most unlikely systems of which we are aware in the universe. As evolution has progressed in the biosphere of the earth, local entropy has decreased rather than increased. Organic molecules have been organized into extremely complex structures. We return to that old paradox: How are we to reconcile the presence of a human brain and the complex neurological pathways of the human nervous system with the contradictory prediction of the second law of thermodynamics? If disorder and disorganization must eventually inherit the universe, how did we come about?

But, we are not an isolated system living on the surface of our little planet. The second law applies to a complete and closed system, and our ecosystem is truly cosmic in extent. We depend upon the sun for the synthesis performed by green plants, and to a degree which is not usually appreciated, we depend upon the space between the galaxies to absorb our waste products. Like all successful ecosystems, we need both an energy source and a means of waste disposal. Without the bright sun on one side and dark space on the other, we would not continue to exist. Our precarious perch between hot and cold is not accidental, for we could survive nowhere else in the cosmos.

Our thermodynamic system thus contains two prime ingredients: one hot star and the energy sink of space. In such a system, the total entropy is indeed increasing with time. Photons spill out of the sun into the surrounding space, becoming more dispersed and diluted. The system grows in entropy just as the entropy of the child's room increases as the toys spill out of the toy box. On the earth we grow in complexity because we are able to collect the minutest fraction of those photons produced by the sun's surface at a high temperature and then convert them into photons of a much lower temperature which are radiated by us people and our surroundings. This degradation of the energy of the photons and their eventual dispersal into space increases the entropy of the entire system, even though a portion of it becomes more complex.

The space which surrounds us devours photons like a pride of hungry lions, and we need that voracious eater of energy as much as we need a local source of energy. Were we surrounded by walls which perfectly reflected rather than perfectly absorbed, no energy would escape from our immediate vicinity and the temperature of our planet would rise from its present value to one which would be in equilibrium with the sun, somewhat hotter than a few thousand degrees. At such a temperature the fragile biochemical molecules of life would dissociate; molecular bonds which glue atoms together can not stand such heat.

The molecular synthesis which has been occurring on our planet for the last 4 billion years is thus "fixed" by the absorbing walls of space just as one preserves the image by fixing the photographic film. Our biosphere is maintained because there is something "out there" which accepts all the energy which flows into it. When space beyond the earth is included in our system, the entropy of the total system has increased even though complex life has formed on the earth.

What allows the space lying between galaxies to be such an insatiable eater of energy? Will it ever fill up and allow the energy density of the universe to increase to an unbearable level? Such questions are related to the curious darkness of the sky at night. One can go outside at night and without any million-dollar telescope make a cosmological observation of profound significance. If the universe were filled uniformly with stars stretching out in all directions to infinity, if those stars have always been present, and if they are not moving relative to the earth, then our sky at night should be brilliantly lighted. In every direction from the earth a line of sight should eventually reach the surface of some star, no matter how far, and our sky should be filled both day and night with surfaces of stars packed tightly like mosaic tile. Ours would not be a succession of days and nights, but instead our heavens would be a blinding wall of light. No sunsets would offer any respite from the awful inpouring of energy. For, given enough time, the space between stars should reach equilibrium with the stars, and the universe should be a vast oven.

But the sky is dark at night and we are not living in an oven. Does that mean that the universe is limited in space or in time? In 1826 when Heinrich Olbers first pointed out the cosmological significance of the darkness of the night sky, he suggested that there may be sufficient dust between the stars to absorb the energy and prevent the temperature of the universe from reaching its equilibrium value. But, that dust should also increase in temperature until it will begin to radiate as much energy as it is absorbing, and we are back where we started except that now we have a hot, *dirty* oven.

The real solution to the paradox lies in the apparent fact that the universe is expanding, evidenced by the red shifts of galaxies which lie beyond our local cluster of galaxies. The universe is indeed an oven, but a very ineffective one. It is surely not one any self-respecting baker would choose, for though the walls are hot, they are moving away from each other. The obvious consequence is that the temperature in the interior never has a chance to reach its equilibrium value, and a cool, pleasant non-equilibrium is maintained inside.

What exactly are these expanding walls? They are the superstructure of space upon which matter hangs. The red-shifted galaxies act only as lighted buoys which identify the structure of underlying space. As space expands these markers are carried along with it. Were it not for these clusters of galaxies, we would be ignorant of the steady expansion of the drain into which pours all the radiative energy of the stars. As that space gets ever larger and larger, it acts as a thermodynamic sink which will never fill up as long as the expansion continues. It will drink and then drink some more, never allowing equilibrium to occur while it is increasing in size (see Figure 4).

We are children born out of equilibrium and, to a degree which is awesome, we rely each second of our days upon the continued disruption of equilibrium. In equilibrium there is a detailed and precise balance between opposing processes. Each process which might, for instance, produce a condensation of matter is opposed by an equal and opposite process. When equilibrium is disrupted, one particular force may predominate and a precipitate of matter may

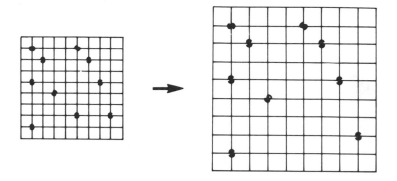

FIGURE 4. The expanding gridwork of space.

occur. Rain falls, snow flakes form, trees grow, and babies are born only in non-equilibrium states.

Although we teach the equations of equilibrium in our physics courses and seek equilibrium in our societies, there is little that is new in that state. When opposing processes are perfectly balanced there is no excitement, no creative re-structuring, no growth of new and surprising low entropy structures. Time does not flow in an equilibrium ocean. There is no river to step into which is different with each step. Only when the system is pushed out of equilibrium and seeks to return, does the river begin to flow. When it is forced into an unlikely condition, the system tries to move toward a more probable state; such is the origin of the second law of thermodynamics. In seeking the more probable but less organized condition, movement and change give birth to time.

As photons flow outward from a star the universe is seeking balance. When a pan of water is forced out of equilibrium by the heat of the stove, water moves in a direction to re-establish a uniform temperature. Let us look more closely at that pan of water, for in the bubbling pot on the stove we can see ourselves reflected.

Initially, before the heat is turned, the system is disordered. Energy is distributed in the random motion of the molecules of water. Equal numbers of molecules ascend and descend; equal numbers move to the right and to the left. But when a large temperature difference occurs between top and bottom, the balance of opposing processes in the fluid is upset. Fluctuations of temperature or density become unstable and rise to the surface of the liquid. When cool they sink to the bottom. The result is a highly ordered pattern of convective flow where some of the energy originally contained in the random motion of the molecules is contained in the ordered motion of convection. Convection persists only so long as the system remains out of equilibrium. Because convective flow is more complex and less probable than random motion, the entropy of the pan of water decreases when convection sets in (see Figure 5).

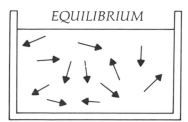

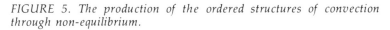

FIGURE 5. *The production of the ordered structures of convection through non-equilibrium.*

The ordered patterns of convection remain as long as the system is forced to remain far from equilibrium by the flame at the bottom of the pan. Once equilibrium is reestablished, the low entropy structures will dissolve. Man and all his biological colleagues on the earth are thus manifestations of the departure of the universe from equilibrium. Like the convection patterns in the pan of water, they will remain only so long that dis-equilibrium is maintained.

As the universe has grown more and more out of equilibrium, it has progressively created grander and more elaborate structures. These structures are measures of the time-fulness of the universe, a timefulness which has direction. We exist now some 15 billion years after the creation of our present universe. In the progression of the universe from the simple to the complex during those 15 billion years, we see the flight of the arrow of time.

We experience that arrow in the irreversibility of our own lives. We move inexorably forward in time, never backward. Never do we grow younger, nor do we see a cup of coffee get warmer while it is sitting on a table. Never do we see high divers rising backward out of the water to land on the diving board, nor do we see air mysteriously move back into a pressure tank. These are all processes which proceed in only one direction along a cosmic one-way street.

7. The River of Time

I do not know much about gods; but I think that the river
Is a strong brown god—sullen, untamed and intractable.
                                T. S. Eliot, "The Dry Salvages"

The arrow of time is both universal and persistent. As far as we can tell, physical processes in other stars and in other galaxies occur in the same time sequence as they do locally. There seems to be no faltering or indecision in the direction in which the arrow points. It has apparently maintained the same directivity during the 15-billion-year lifetime of the universe.

In the original cosmic fireball, only fractions of a second after creation, matter and energy were mixed together in a searing and unfamiliar equilibrium. As space expanded, the average temperature of the universe decreased and in that unfaltering decline in the temperature of the universe, we see flowing river of time.

We have not yet reached the end of the end of time, but we have traversed about 99% of the necessary distance. We are now within approximately 1% of the maximum entropy of the universe. The death of the universe has already occurred and like maggots we inhabit a cooling corpse. But still under a darkening sky the river continues flowing on.

In the twilight of the universe, which occurred only a million years after creation, the temperature had fallen to a few thousand degrees, and matter began to separate from radiation. The first step in the non-equilibrium ordering of the large scale structure of the universe occurred. Radiation moved outward with the expanding structure of space, but matter condensed into the huge granules of proto-galaxies. Stars precipitated out of those huge clouds. In the centers of the stars protons and neutrons came together to create elements which had not before existed. On at least one planet circling a quite ordinary star, the atoms of hydrogen, carbon, nitrogen, and oxygen combined to form large molecules. Finally, man emerged from those molecules.

Throughout the lifetime of our universe there has been a persistence of memory as a progressive modification of matter took place. Each stage grew upon the previous stage, and could not have occurred without the results of prior synthesis. The child needs the supernova which precedes it just as much as it needs its human parents.

In contrast to the sustained change which we see imprinted in the matter of our galaxy, there can be no memory in equilibrium. There is no doubt that if at any time in our past, equilibrium had somehow been established in the universe, the arrow of time would have lost its direction, and the systematic evolution of matter would have ceased.

It is necessary, therefore, that the universe be ever frustrated in its attempts to reach equilibrium. It is alive because it is seeking equilibrium, yet it must never achieve that state for to do so would mean death. If the river of time is to continue flowing only those evolutionary changes can occur which will move the system even further from equilibrium. A positive feedback loop must operate such that each newly formed structure encourages continued evolution by further increasing the departure from equilibrium (see Figure 6).

The evolution of a star provides us with an example of such sustained evolution driven forward by positive feedback. The star begins its career as an unstable density fluctuation in the interstellar gas. Because the gas is not in perfect equilibrium, the processes opposing condensation are not as effective as those encouraging the clumping of matter, and a fluctuation in the density of the gas rapidly grows. More matter in the condensation causes a stronger gravitational force and consequently even more material is drawn in; the density increases exponentially with time.

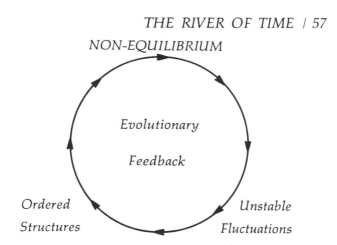

FIGURE 6. *Evolutionary feedback loop. Equilibrium is increasingly disrupted by ordered structures which results in enhanced fluctuations and further growth of order.*

The spheres of gas continue to contract under their self-gravity and eventually acquire temperatures of several million degrees in their cores due to the conversion of gravitational energy to thermal energy. The modest ball of gas becomes a bona fide star when such a temperature is reached and it begins to generate energy through the conversion of hydrogen to helium. At this stage the non-equilibrium of the mixture of gas and stars is more extreme than when there was only gas. A significant fraction of the matter of the original gas cloud is collected into the large density and temperature fluctuations which we call stars. The entropy of this collection of stars is less than the entropy of the initial homogenous gas. If the entropy of the stars is to continue decreasing, there must be encouragement for even greater departures from equilibrium. But first the star rests for a period amounting to more than 90% of the star's lifetime, during which inward directed gravitational pressure is balanced by outward directed thermal pressure. This state of quasi-equilibrium lasts as long as there is sufficient hydrogen in the core to feed the thermonuclear furnace.

The core contains only 10% of the mass of the star, and once the hydrogen of the core is exhausted, the star again seeks equilibrium by contracting. But contraction aggravates its dilemma and only serves to drive it further from equilibrium as the temperature and density of the core increase. When a temperature of approximately 100 million degrees is reached in the core, three helium nuclei can start to combine with each other to produce carbon as ash. The new energy source gives the star a brief respite in its search for equilibrium. However, the period of helium burning is briefer than that of hydrogen burning, and soon the star begins to contract again. It pauses at a temperature of 800 million degrees to burn carbon; then again in its ever accelerating collapse it pauses at 2 billion degrees to burn oxygen.

If the star has a mass which is three or more times that of the sun, it will continue driving itself further and further from equilibrium until eventually it blows itself to smithereens as a supernova. In such explosions where the material has a temperature between 2 and 8 billion degrees, most of the elements heavier than calcium on our planet may have been created.

The galaxy contains evidence of many such violent and explosive events in the form of pulsars, x-ray sources, and variable radio sources. In multiple star systems, the rate of evolution is accelerated with the result that such systems apparently house remnants of violently non-equilibrium processes such as pulsars and x-ray stars. The discoveries of the last few years have demonstrated that extreme departures from equilibrium are not uncommon and may play major roles in the evolution of the material of the galaxy.

For those stars with mass less than three times that of the sun-death, quietude, and equilibrium come in the white dwarf stage. In such low mass stars the gravitational pressure is balanced by the same quantum mechanical forces which prevent an atom from collapsing. Unable to synthesize any new elements, the white dwarfs slowly and quietly sink into equilibrium and obscurity.

All systems with temperatures above absolute zero have fluctuations in density, pressure, temperature, energy, etc. Near equilibrium these fluctuations are damped by opposing forces which establish balance. As the system moves further from equilibrium the balancing processes become less effective and at some stage, the fluctuations become unstable and will grow and amplify, culminating in the case of the massive star in the final catastrophe of the supernova.

Balanced, non-amplified fluctuations lead nowhere. If each new burst of element production drove the star closer to equilibrium rather than farther away, stars could not have progressed through suggestive instabilities to produce the building blocks of life. The development of a star is similar to the development of other low entropy structures in the universe, all of which rely upon the non-equilibrium produced by the expansion of space. If entropy is to continue decreasing new structures must be produced which will drive small regions of the universe even farther from equilibrium.

Parallel to the formation of complex structures through this process of positive feedback, there has been a miniaturization of complexity. As time has advanced, information has flowed from macroscopic structures to microscopic structures. At the beginning of the universe the entropy associated with the largest scale structure, the universe itself, was at a minimum. As the universe expanded and smaller and smaller structures developed, information has become increasingly concentrated in these small structures. Thus while the entropy of the macrocosm has grown due to the expansion of space and the dilution of energy, the entropy of the microcosm has actually decreased.

When matter separated from radiation and galaxies formed, the lowest entropy structures were galactic in size, a few million light years across. Then stars formed, and being more complicated than galaxies, the size of the most complex structures dropped to stellar dimensions, a few million kilometers. Once life started forming on planets, there was an enormous increase in the complexity of small biological structures. And now, the human brain, one foot in diameter, represents the minimum entropy structure in the universe. Meanwhile, the entropy of all structures larger than the human brain has been increasing. It is difficult to see where this process of the miniaturization of complexity will go from here.

Future expansion without end: is this our future? As the entropy of the macrocosm approaches its maximum, stars and galaxies will one by one grow dim and wink out as their nuclear fuel is irreversibly exhausted. Is it an infinitely long funeral which lies ahead? If expansion continues and the average temperature of the universe approaches absolute zero, even the smallest structures will lose their vitality. Perhaps it will take 50 billion years or 100 billion years but unless expansion is reversed the conclusion seems unavoidable: dark cinders moving silently in a dead cosmos.

It is presently impossible to decide from the current astronomical evidence whether or not expansion will be reversed. Around 1970 most astronomers probably favored a closed universe which oscillated from fireball to fireball. In the last few years, however, astronomers have become increasingly doubtful that there is sufficient matter in the universe to cause it to oscillate. Since gravity is the process which must pull galaxies back together in the contracting phase, the problem comes down to estimating the density of matter in the universe.

It should be a simple task to count the number of galaxies within a certain volume of the neighboring universe, estimate their mass, and hence determine the mass density of visible matter. Such galaxies contribute less than 5% of the material necessary to stop expansion of the universe. There may be dark, undetected matter lying between the galaxies, but it appears doubtful that there is enough dark stuff to cause the universe to oscillate.

We find ourselves in a very frustrating situation. The distinction between oscillation or eternal expansion has enormous philosophical consequences, is based upon a single number, and yet cannot be made because of the present lack of observational data. It is all the more tantalizing because we seem so close to the answer; the small uncertainty remaining in our determination of the mass density could push the universe into either model. But, whatever the outcome, it seems clear that we will still be living in a changing universe, swinging back and forth or steadily moving toward a death of cold and darkness.

8. The Cosmic Couple and the Golden Egg

Here the impossible union
Of spheres of existence is actual,
Here the past and future
Are conquered, and reconciled . . .
T. S. Eliot, "The Dry Salvages"

In the creation mythologies involving the deities of the earth and sky, there is a curious reluctance on the part of the gods to continue with the work of creation. The gods early in the game abandon the initiative and actually set themselves in opposition to the continuing development of the world.

Contained in these myths is a remarkable sense of the great mystery of our changing existence and the recognition of the uncreativity of equilibrium. A stable equilibrium such as formed by the union of polar opposites is self-maintaining and all tendencies to change are countered by opposing forces.

In the Polynesian story, for instance, the gods just refuse to stop their love making:

> According to the traditions of our race, Rangi and Papa, or Heaven and Earth, were the source from which in the beginning all things originated. Darkness then rested upon the heaven and upon the earth, and they still both clave together, for they had not yet been rent apart; and the children they had begotten were ever thinking amongst themselves what might be the difference between darkness and light; they knew that

beings had multiplied and increased, and yet light had never broken upon them, but it ever continued dark.

The problem is that the happy couple is too content just lying together. Their union harmonizes all the opposing and antagonistic aspects of the universe and cannot be improved upon. The equilibrium which results from the joining of earth and sky has stopped the flow of time because the present moment is too perfect. What more could the gods desire; what more could they possibly want or need? The earth mother can be infinitely coy, for indeed she does have time and world enough. Nothing remains to be done in a universe in which the two polar opposites are so completely reconciled.

This theme of the inert primordial couple is repeated in many creation mythologies, for the infatuation of the world parents was recognized as one of the first great barriers to creation. In the Babylonian creation epic, Apsu and Tiamat are described as "co-mingling as a single body" in unformed darkness, very content to stay together. Likewise in the cuneiform Sumerian texts there is the same imagery of unified opposites as An, the sky father, and Ki, the earth mother, lie together. In the creation story given by Hesiod, Uranos and Gaia are joined in semi-permanent primordial equilibrium.

But during their long embrace these couples have produced noisy and bothersome children. In the Babylonian story, Apsu complains of his children:

> Their ways are verily loathsome unto me. By day I find no relief, nor repose by night. I will destroy. I will wreck their ways, that quiet may be restored. Let us have rest!

The children in turn have become exasperated with the inactivity of their parents. It is excruciatingly tedious; their parents never do anything, never go anywhere. The children do not appreciate being crushed between their parents' bellies. There is a feeling of terrible urgency on the part of the children to break out of their prison and to separate their parents. Time needs to break into the non-time and non-change of equilibrium.

> They (the children) were in an unstable condition, floating about the world of darkness, and this was their appearance: some were crawling . . . some were upright with arms held up . . . some lying on their sides . . . some on their backs, some were stooping, some with their heads bent down, some with legs drawn up . . . some kneeling . . . some falling about in the dark. . . . They were all within the embrace of Rangi and Papa.

So the children get together and plot to sabotage the marital bliss of their parents. It is the old story of creatures who feel unable to express their own uniqueness because of the oppressive forces which hold them down. The children must push apart the layers of the primordial sandwich, and by separating earth and sky allow light and change to enter their realm.

> At last the beings who had been begotten by Heaven and Earth, worn out by the continued darkness, consulted among themselves, saying, "Let us now determine what we should do with Rangi and Papa, whether it would be better to slay them or to rend them apart." Then spake Tumagauenga, the fiercest of the children of Earth and Heaven, "It is well, let us slay them." Then spake Tanemahuta, the father of the forests and of all things that inhabit them, or that are constructed from trees. "Nay, not so. It is better to rend them apart, and to let the heaven stand far above us, and the earth lie under our feet. Let the sky become a stranger to us, but the earth remain close to us as our nursing mother."

Although most of the brothers agree to attempt to separate their parents, none can be found who would consent to do it. Finally several try unsuccessfully until at last Tanemahuta himself gives it a try.

> . . . his head is now firmly planted on his mother, the earth, his feet he raises up and rests against his father the skies, he strains his back and limbs with a mighty effort. Now are rent apart Rangi and Papa, and with cries and groans of woe they shriek aloud, "Wherefore slay you thus your parents? Why commit you so dreadful a crime as to slay us, as to rend your parents apart?" But Tanemahuta pauses not, he regards not their shrieks and cries; far, far beneath him he presses down the earth; far, far above him he thrusts up the sky."

In the Egyptian story of creation, the roles of male and female are reversed but the theme is the same. The mother is the sky. The father is the fecund earth. The two are separated by their child the air god Shu (see Figure 7).

Equilibrium is upset by the aggressive and impatient children and space expands. The tension and energy of the cosmos is built up by the separation of the parts. Although the parents desperately wish to be together as in the old days, they are prevented from returning to equilibrium, for that would again return the universe to darkness and death. Non-equilibrium must be maintained at all costs.

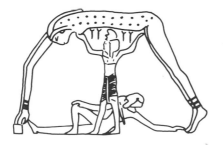

FIGURE 7. The Separation of Sky and Earth

In some cases, mere pushing is not enough. The extreme inertia and passivity of the primordial couple require an extreme effort on the part of the children. The parents resist and must be fought and eventually slaughtered by their children. In the Babylonian epic of creation, the sun god Marduk must slay the mother of the gods, Tiamat. Once the mother, but now the menace of the world, she is a terrifying dragon-like personification of the darkness of chaos.

> [Marduk] seized the trident and burst her belly. He severed her inward parts; he pierced her heart. He overcame her and cut off her life; he cast down her body and stood on it. . . . And the lord stood upon Tiamat's hinder parts, and with his merciless club he smashed her skull. . . . Then the lord rested, gazing on her dead body . . . and devised a cunning plan. He split her up like a flat fish into two halves; one half of her he established as a covering for heaven.

It would seem that Marduk rather overplayed his role in the bloody slaughter of his mother, but such excess was necessary to insure that equilibrium and darkness would never again fall upon the cosmos. He pushed back the dark waters with a ceiling above and a floor beneath, and in that newly formed space he created man. His struggle represented the victory of order over chaos, as light entered that space which was initially dark and formless.

The separation or slaughter of the parents and the subsequent rise to power of their progeny does not mean the total disappearance of the old gods of darkness. The new universe is constructed out of their bodies. They continue to exist as a residue in their old kingdom which has now become blindingly bright.

It is remarkable the extent to which we have in the world-parent mythologies essentially all the ingredients of our modern cosmology. In modern theory the darkness and equilibrium which blanketed the beginning of the world were eliminated by the big bang and the subsequent expansion of space. The non-equilibrium which resulted from the separation of primordial matter allowed the creation of the complex structures of the microcosm. The world-parent myth also resembles current speculations about the presence of large amounts of anti-matter in the early universe. The annihilation of that anti-matter less than a few seconds after creation of the universe may have produced the light of the primordial fireball.

Before discussing the modern theory for the fireball of creation let me quickly review the characteristics of anti-matter. Until the discovery of the anti-electron by Carl Anderson in 1932, the universe appeared to be disturbingly unsymmetrical. The proton, electron, and neutron had been discovered and had appeared to be the fundamental constituents of matter. The neutron is electrically neutral. It and the positively charged proton are 1846 times heavier than the negatively charged electron. Although the charges on the electron and proton are exactly equal and oppositive, the masses of the two particles give no hint of symmetry. From an aesthetic viewpoint, it was unfortunate that there were no negatively charged heavy particles and no positively charged light particles.

Then, following the prediction by P. A. M. Dirac of electron "holes," Anderson discovered the positive electron. It has precisely the same mass as the ordinary electron and an equal but opposite charge. In 1952 when sufficient energy was available in particle accelerators, the anti-proton was created. Now it appears that every known particle has an anti-particle of the same mass and opposite charge.

Anti-particles and particles are produced in equal numbers in the process known as pair production, which occurs whenever $2mc^2$ of energy is squeezed into a sufficiently small space. Energy goes in and out pops an electron and a positron or a proton and an anti-proton. The reverse process of annihilation occurs when an anti-particle and a particle come together and convert each other into $2mc^2$ worth of energy.

A positron and an anti-proton can be brought together to form an anti-atom of positronium. The anti-proton becomes a negatively charged nucleus and the positron spins around it. The radiation produced by positronium is indistinguishable from that produced by hydrogen. A star composed of such material could generate energy through the fusion of positronium producing anti-helium as a product. An anti-star composed of sufficiently large mass could produce the anti-matter counterparts of all ninety-two stable chemical elements. Out of the material of such an anti-star, positronium and anti-oxygen could join to form anti-water which would have all the physical and chemical properties of ordinary water. It would freeze at 0° C and boil at 100° C and would fall as anti-snow flakes to collect on anti-glaciers on the surfaces of anti-planets. The entire sequence of evolution of life on the earth could be paralleled by the development of anti-matter resulting in anti-people living in houses built of anti-matter. In our own world anti-matter never has a chance to develop into complex atoms or molecules because it is so quickly annihilated by matter.

The lack of symmetry of matter and anti-matter in the universe has not been resolved simply by the demonstration that we can create occasional short-lived bits of anti-matter in our laboratories or our atmosphere. The puzzle remains why the possibility of anti-matter should be allowed in the microcosm but not permitted in the macrocosm. We are living on a planet made of matter in a solar system similarly made of matter. There is one very remote possibility that a meteorite of anti-matter passed through the solar system and may have crashed into the earth producing the great explosion which occurred in Siberia in 1908. But the general lack of appropriate fireworks in our solar system indicates the absence of any sizeable clump of anti-matter in our immediate vicinity.

The situation is somewhat different beyond the solar system. When matter and anti-matter occupy different regions, they are optically indistinguishable from each other. An isolated anti-star or a remote globular cluster composed of anti-stars might persist for some time at the edge of our galaxy. But it is doubtful that in the densely populated central regions of the galaxy there can be many anti-stars. So the riddle remains. There may be an occasional bit of anti-matter in our galaxy, but matter seems clearly favored.

As I have mentioned, it has been suggested that the early universe may have contained large amounts of matter. At the high temperatures and densities which existed just after creation, both matter and anti-matter should have been created in great abundance due to pair production. The picture we have of those awesome first moments is of matter and anti-matter thoroughly mixed together, continually cycling between the state of matter and the state of energy: annihilation chasing pair production round and round in a circle. However, as space expanded, the temperature of the sea of energy decreased so that pair production was unable to keep up with annihilation. First, about .0001 seconds after creation, the heavy particles such as protons and neutrons annihilated their counterparts in a burst of light which was not followed by replenishment through pair production. The density of energy was too low to create pairs of protons and anti-protons. Then about 10 seconds later, the lighter particles such as electrons and mesons annihilated their anti-siblings in another great burst of radiation. At this stage the universe was a sea of light, brilliant but too thin to continue producing pairs of particles. This was the golden egg of myth, the fireball of creation which has continued expanding and cooling to its present temperature of 2.7 degrees above absolute zero.

The number of creation mythologies that describe an abrupt emergence of light or the appearance of a brilliant golden egg is striking. In the Orphic creation myth, the world started with a silver egg; in the Chandogya Upanishad creation is associated with a half-silver half-gold egg. The silver part became the earth; that which was of gold became heaven. In the Brahman story involving the first man,

Prajapati, a golden egg floated on the cosmic ocean for a year before producing the world. In Chinese legend, pure light came out of dark chaos. And in the Egyptian story, the sun emerged from the primeval ocean. In each of these the theme is similar to that associated with the separation of the primordial parents. Light, which is symbolic of order and knowledge, emerges from chaos. The egg is, of course, a natural symbol for the source of life and the incubator of the world.

In the account of creation from the Upanishads, the membrane of the white became the mountains, the veins became the river, and the fluid in the egg became the ocean. In the fireball of modern cosmology, precisely equal amounts of matter and anti-matter could not have been inter-mixed, for in the resulting total annihilation of the mixture only light would have emerged. No mountains, rivers, or ocean, only photons would inhabit the corridors of space. No stars would punctuate the background and no macro-molecules would become self-aware.

But there are stars and there is a human audience. All of this suggests that in that fireball which is our honored ancestor, there may have been an excess of matter over anti-matter. It is surprising, actually, how slight an error in cosmic arithmetic could account for our presence. We can estimate the original amount of matter and anti-matter in the original universe by counting the photons given off as primordial matter annihilated primordial anti-matter. We see those photons as the 2.7° K radiation which falls upon the earth like rain from all directions. The earth is still immersed in the fireball of creation, and although the light is much fainter and much redder than it was at the beginning, practically every photon from that initial big bang is still present.

The tallying of the photons is a humbling experience, for it turns out that matter is an embarrassingly insignificant ingredient of the universe. For every particle of matter, including every bit of material we can imagine (stars, elephants, interstellar clouds, black holes, etc.) there are approximately a billion photons of light. We are still living in an ocean of light in which matter floats as a very thinly distributed flotsam.

An original error of one part in a billion, one millionth of one percent could account for our presence in the universe. Thus for every billion particles which existed in the original fireball, there may have been one extra maverick particle of matter. We are indeed grateful for the initial mistake in arithmetic, if such was the case. Without it the universe would be so much less interesting: no stars, no people, nothing but that dim illumination which has now fallen to a temperature only a few degrees above absolute zero.

An incredibly small mistake in the original distribution of particles is a fascinating possibility, but it is not altogether satisfactory. There is still awkwardness in this postulate of an ever so slight departure from symmetry. We are rarely that accurate in arithmetic, but one expects better of the creator.

An alternate possibility is that matter and anti-matter were indeed precisely equal in number in the original fireball, but that they were clumped together in different regions of space. As the universe expanded the clumps of matter pulled themselves together to form galaxies; the other clumps became anti-galaxies. The consequences are clear: the universe should contain roughly equal numbers of anti-galaxies and galaxies. Half of the galaxies we can photograph from the earth may be composed of anti-matter protons and positrons. Half of the intelligent creatures in the universe may be such that we would never care to fraternize with them.

At present we cannot decide between these two possibilities. There are violent phenomena in the universe which could be the result of large clouds of matter annihilating equally large clouds of anti-matter. Some galaxies give the appearance of having been rocked by explosions which may have been the consequence of annihilation of galactic substructures composed of anti-matter. Whether the earth mother and the sky father remain as a luminous residue cooled almost beyond recognition or dismembered as hundreds of billions of galaxies and anti-galaxies is a question remaining for our future excursions in cosmology.

9. A Journey to the Edge of Time

> So the darkness shall be the light, and the
> stillness the dancing
> > T. S. Eliot, "East Coker"

Astronomers have always been blessed by possessing a sense of freedom with respect to space and time. Never having to worry about the bothersome details of air fares, motel reservations, or traffic jams, we can deal with immense distances in the universe simply by staying at home close to our telescopes. Photons of light, well-traveled and old, come to us as prey comes to the hunter. A glance at the sun, our brightest star, takes us back eight minutes in time, for light requires those minutes to cross the space separating the earth from the sun.

I shall attempt some time travel using the wandering photons and a little astrophysical theory. Since everywhere beyond the earth lies past time, to move out from the earth is to move backward in time. Let us leave the earth, gathering up ever more ancient photons as we venture further from our home.

Off we go: past Mars, beyond the crumbling asteroids, we reach Jupiter lying some forty minutes in the earth's past. With not quite enough matter to be a star, it remained a giant among planets rather than a dwarf among stars. Practically unchanged in chemical composition since the time of the origin of the solar system, this spinning ball of swirling gasses is stuck in time as an arrested proto-star. Having retained practically all of its original constituents,

Jupiter is as our sun was over four billion years ago before it started transmuting elements in its core.

Continuing outward beyond the outermost planet of the solar system, Pluto, more than five hours in the earth's past, we leave the solar system to begin the long and lonely journey from star to star. The sun has dwindled noticeably in brightness, looking cool and distant like Venus hovering above a winter horizon. We plunge into the dim, vacant interstellar spaces.

It takes light four years to reach the sun's nearest neighbors, a triple star system of which the brightest is Alpha Centauri. We cut upwards toward the galactic pole, and in a few thousand light years reach the edge of the galaxy. Behind us the sky is filled with stars, like a lighted city at night reaching from horizon to horizon. Ahead, the sky is black; a desert blacker than any darkness we have ever experienced. It is as if we were back on the earth in the mountains at night with a heavy overcast. An occasional globular cluster hangs away from the disk of stars of the galaxy, but except for those ancient stars, there is nothing that is luminous between us and the next spiral galaxy.

Moving through that emptiness, the insignificance of matter in our universe becomes only too clear, and the effect is gently minimizing. The universe is large and the rare concentrations of matter are tiny by comparison with the distances which separate them. In the intergalactic spaces we float like grotesque fish deep in the ocean meeting only an occasional spinning galaxy moving silently through the darkness. The few galaxies we are able to detect during our travels are as struggling candles in the huge temple of space-time. There is so much more space than matter that we can travel tens of millions of years between encounters with other galaxies.

As we continue to move back in time, we notice a slow change in our surroundings. Fewer and fewer galaxies pass into our vision, and we eventually arrive at a time when matter has not yet condensed into galaxies. The darkness is complete and unbroken; we have reached a time perhaps ten to fifteen billion years in the past. The entire universe consists of a thin broth of photons, ghostly neutrinos, protons, electrons, and a very small number of alpha particles, the nuclei of helium atoms.

We continue moving backward through the unstructured darkness. Gradually we sense another change in our surroundings. It does not seem as dark as before. There is a faint diffuse glow of light coming from all directions. The light has come upon us so gradually that it seems it must have been here all the time but we failed to realize it.

Now we can see more clearly in the dim light; it is as if we were approaching a sunrise before which all the lights of our memory pale into insignificance. The entire cosmos is one sun, which becomes brighter and brighter as we continue moving back toward the beginning.

We reach the photosphere of the universe and we enter it as if we were sliding beneath the surface of the sun. We have come upon the fabled golden egg glowing with the annihilation radiation from the original matter and antimatter. The time is one million years after the creation of the universe and we find ourselves swimming in a sea of light with a temperature of several thousands of degrees. The spectacle is similar to that described in the eleventh chapter of the *Bhagavad-Gita* when Krishna reveals to Arjuna the uncountable suns of his infinite form:

"Ah, my God!" said Arjuna to the Lord Krishna, "I see all gods within your body . . . eyes shrink from your splendor, brilliant like the sun, like fire, blazing, boundless. Firey-faced you blast the world to ashes. Licking with your burning tongues, devouring all the worlds, you probe the heights of heaven with intolerable beams . . ."

Formed at a time when the density of the universe was a billion times larger than now, the primordial fireball has all the properties of a stellar photosphere except that we are living inside it rather than looking at it from a distance. These glowing walls which surround us on all sides and which block our vision to earlier times, lie at a distance of 10 to 15 billion light years and are exceedingly dull. Indeed one of the strangest properties of the universe is the uniformity of that ancient red-shifted cosmic photosphere. Wherever we look in our sky, the temperature we measure is always 2.7 degrees above absolute zero. Recent measurements have shown that the uniformity of that temperature is remarkable. We cannot be living, for instance, near the edge of the universe, for were that the case we should see some dimming of the radiation in that direction. The most puzzling aspect of that uniformity is that all parts of the cosmic photosphere cannot be aware of each other and cannot, therefore, be causally connected. Light which is just now reaching us from one direction of the sky has not yet had a chance to encounter that portion of the photosphere which lies in an opposite direction. Neither region has thus had an opportunity to interact with the other, and to come into equilibrium. Yet the temperature of those far distant regions is equal to within the accuracy of our measurements. None of our cosmological theories has yet produced a satisfactory explanation of this uniformity of the background radiation.

Like the photosphere of our sun, the photosphere of the universe masks the radiation which lies behind it. It also marks a profound change in the status of radiation in the universe. Before the cosmic photosphere came into existence radiation and matter were so tightly coupled together that after a photon was emitted by an atom or an ion, it was almost immediately reabsorbed. Due to the continued expansion of space and the consequent decline in the density of the universe, photons eventually became uncoupled from matter. This decrease in the density of both matter and radiation transformed the universe from a murky fluid which was opaque to radiation, to one which was clear and transparent in which photons could travel anywhere just as long as they did not bump into the relatively rare surfaces of planets or stars. The clearing took place 400,000 years ago and produced the edge of the cosmic photosphere.

Our optical shovels can thus not dig any deeper into the past than the photon barrier of the photosphere: electromagnetic waves cannot carry us beyond this cage, 400,000 years old, which isolates us from the earlier universe. In order to penetrate this barrier we need a process which interacts less strongly with matter than does light.

The modest neutrino comes to our rescue. Invented by Wolfgang Pauli in 1930, the neutrino escaped direct detection until 1956. With no rest mass and no charge, it is an elusive object which can slip like a ghost through vast amounts of matter. A wall of concrete at least 3,500 light years thick is needed to absorb one. Here, then, is the ideal guide for further exploration of the early universe.

However, our exploration can be only by means of theory, for we have not yet been able to detect neutrinos from the early universe.

Our theoretical models of the universe earlier than the cosmic photosphere indicate that in that increasingly dense and hot collection of particles and energy, even neutrinos found it difficult to travel very far without being absorbed. At .0001 seconds in fact there occurred a neutrino barrier similar to the photon barrier which was formed 400,000 years later. Perhaps an even more elusive particle such as the graviton could pass freely through the universe at that time. Gravitons are the particles associated with the phenomenon of gravity and have not yet been detected because it is so extraordinarily difficult to capture one. Gravity is not appreciably absorbed by any material in our present universe and for that reason we have not yet been able to build an anti-gravity shield. These as yet undetected gravitons however are strongly predicted by theory, and perhaps some day we shall be able to build a graviton detector which can "see" gravitons created soon after the universe was born.

In that universe beyond the neutrino barrier, hot and dense beyond our experience and imagination, alien forms must have existed which were smaller than the protons, neutrons, and electrons which make up our current world. Our protons are too large to have fitted into that extremely dense universe, in which only smaller, denser particles could have existed.

These particles which existed close to the beginning had a problem which we fortunately we do not have: they were close to falling into a black hole of their own making. A black hole is surrounded by an event horizon which separates it from the surrounding universe, and these very young particles were only slightly larger than their event horizons.

The very earliest particles which existed in our universe are called *archeons:* the mythic parents of all matter. The detailed characteristics of archeons are not known other than their mass which was some 10^{20} times larger than that of a proton. They existed only briefly 10^{-43} seconds after creation and decayed almost immediately into particles with lower mass. Unless there is some region of the universe in which time has stood still, we would not expect any archeons to have survived to the present time.

Beyond 10^{-43} seconds, there were no particles. In fact, there was no physics. The structure of space and time was totally disorganized, and the only particle-like objects which might have been present would have been smaller than their event horizons. This period of the universe known as *Primordial Chaos* could be described as a dark sea of black holes. But even that does not do justice to the quality of chaos which existed. During this time the universe was so young that one side of a black hole could not have known that the other side existed. Insufficient time had elapsed for information to travel across the black holes which existed at that time. Thus not only were the black holes ignorant of the existence of their neighbors but they were ignorant of themselves. The actors of our cosmic drama have hidden themselves under invisible capes and the stage upon which they might have walked has crumbled into pieces.

Primordial chaos, impenetrable by our physics, is the terra incognita of modern cosmology. Such a confrontation with ignorance is an experience our current cosmology shares with many ancient cosmologies and creation myths. This imagery of chaos lying at the beginning of time is an extraordinarily widespread element in creation mythologies. Darkness and water are often employed to symbolize an ignorance and absence of form which preceded our world. Water has the quality of being without structure and yet having played a role in the creation of structure. It carries the terror of self-disintegration and the promise of rebirth.

In the Babylonian story of creation one encounters not only darkness and water, but also an assortment of strange and deformed creatures, not too unlike those figments of our modern-day imagination which we call quarks, archeons, and gravitons:

> He says there was a time in which all was darkness and water wherein strange and peculiarly shaped creatures came into being. There were born men with two wings, some also with four wings and two faces . . . and dogs with fourfold bodies and the tails of fish; also horses with the heads of dogs; and men and other creatures with the heads and bodies of horses and the tails of fish . . .

The Hebrew story of creation similarly starts with water and darkness:

> The earth was without form and void, and darkness was upon the fact of the deep; and the Spirit of God was moving over the face of the waters.

In the *Rig Veda* the ignorance and nothingness which preceded our world are described with extreme thoroughness, leaving no room at all for the presence of anything familiar or substantial:

> There was then neither non-existence nor existence
> There was no air nor sky that is beyond it
> Death existed not nor life immortal
> Of neither night nor day was any token.

From the modern Greek poet comes a most remarkable description of those early few fractions of a second in the life of our universe: "I recall," remarks Nikos Kazantzakis in his *Saviors of God*, "an endless desert of infinite and flaming matter. I am burning. I pass through immeasurable, unorganized time, completely alone, despairing, crying in the wilderness."

There is a sense, both in modern cosmology and in these stories of creation, that chaos is primarily a synonym for ignorance: temporary human ignorance. But, as a well-used symbol, chaos seems to represent more than just a current frontier in our knowledge.

Chaos may lie deep in the fabric of our reality, so deep that it may never be overcome. The Uncertainty Principle of quantum mechanics implies an irrationality and chaos of the world of the *small;* and our discovery of primordial chaos implies an irrationality of the *early*. Perhaps both are simply aspects of a world which is larger than human reason.

10. Ascent from the Abyss

The only hope, or else despair
Lies in the choice of pyre or pyre—
To be redeemed from fire by fire.
T. S. Eliot, "Little Giddings

Now that we have ventured to the edge of chaos, let us return to the present, tracing in both myth and science the development of the universe from this beginning. One of the most ancient of figures found in creation mythologies is that of the Earth Mother who symbolizes all the mysteries of birth, growth, and change. She is that fertile source of life warmed by the sun out of whom all the magic of creation emerges. In some obscure way all the complexity and beauty of the present world are contained in her mysterious form.

She represents the potential for unlimited creation which existed at the beginning of time, part of which has now become manifest through the complex process of evolution. In the imagery used by Nikos Kazantzakis, God is locked up inside of matter, using every possible strategy to break out of his prison and continue the work of converting matter into spirit.

In the emergence myths of the Hopi, Navaho, and Pueblo cultures, that conversion of matter into spirit is described in terms of an upward climb through four lower worlds. Nonhuman creatures are transformed into humans who advance toward oneness and harmony. The lowest of the four worlds is black and is distinguished by an ominous sense of disorder and chaos. The motion of that world produces dizziness and disorientation in the vaguely defined creatures who are attempting to move upward. In that lowest of all places, the early creatures possessed no social institutions, were addicted to sorcery and were wife stealers besides.

Moving upward into the next higher world they resolve to cooperate and live in peace with the inhabitants of that world. But they never succeed. And rightly so, for each of the lower worlds is unsuitable in one way or another and they must not be allowed to become permanent residents of those incomplete places. Disequilibrium must always be maintained so that the natural course of evolution can continue. In the Hanelthnayhe myth of the Navaho, women manage to provide that necessary push to evolution, for the female inhabitants of the lower worlds become involved in various adulterous adventures with the visitors. After they have reached the second world, a blue one, they live happily for twenty-three days among the Swallow People:

> But on the twenty-fourth night one of the strangers made too free with the wife of the Swallow chief, and next morning, when the latter found out what had happened, he said to the strangers: "We have treated you as friends, and thus you return our kindness. We doubt not that for such crimes you were driven from the lower world, and now you must leave this."

The next world was colored yellow and in it lived the Grasshopper People. Again, the same series of events repeated itself. As in the lower world all went well for twenty-three days, but on the twenty-fourth day again adultery was discovered by the chief of the Grasshoppers. "For such crimes," he said, "I suppose you were chased from the world below; you shall drink no more of our water, you shall breathe no more of our air. Begone!"

The effect of adultery is similar to that of the slaughter of the cosmic parents by their restless children. Through their adultery women provide the narrow time and prevent stagnation at the lower levels. Change is sustained for the visitors are never welcome back in those worlds from which they have been ejected.

The goal of upward emergence is a harmonizing of different elements such as color and space. The lower worlds have but one color and one direction. Only the present world is illuminated by integrated white light in a harmony of colors. The initial disorientation is replaced by structured space containing the four directions of the compass marked out by four precious stones.

The place of emergence is a holy and fearful spot. For the Hopi it is the Grand Canyon. In the floor of the Pueblo kiva is the *sipapu,* the place where the ancestors emerged and where the energies of eternity still break into time.

Emergence is a display of great power and vitality as the momentum of evolution has been able to break through the inertia of the unmanifest and unchanging. In our astrophysical version of the emergence myth we can perceive that power in the incredible speeds with which galaxies have been flung out by the act of creation. We have also encountered several of those lower worlds. The lowest is that of chaos: dark, disorganized, marked by ignorance. Above that lies the realm of the cosmic parents, their short-lived bliss ending some ten seconds after creation. The next world contains the golden egg, resplendent in the light produced by the mutual annihilation of matter and anti-matter. During this period which ended approximately one million years after creation, the annihilation processes have stopped and the universe is flooded with photons and neutrinos. Matter is a faint precipitate suspended in the dense brilliant light. The era of the golden egg ends with the photosphere of the universe when space has expanded sufficiently to dilute radiation and uncouple it from matter. Matter is then able to gather together into aggregates which eventually become galaxies.

In this fourth world, the stellar era, two kinds of stars are needed to carry the universe upward along the path of emergence. Stars like our sun must be present to provide a steady and reliable energy source for encircling planets. In addition, supernovae are required. Displaying great ingenuity, each time it runs out of one kind of fuel the star re-tools its engine so that it can utilize a new kind of fuel requiring a higher temperature. The result is a steady increase in the number of heavy elements in its interior and a rise in the temperature of the star which eventually leads to instability and death.

In the explosion the star fails in its task of being a star, but succeeds in ways which transcend the star. It scatters itself and the newly formed elements throughout the surrounding galaxy. Out of that enriched gas new stars are born which are different from all those which preceded them for they and their planets contain the stuff of life. The new elements can be put together in a variety of ways which were impossible with hydrogen alone. Whatever its alien form or bizarre shape, life was out of the question before the first explosion of a supernova.

The process of molecular bonding necessary to advance to the next stage of evolution cannot take place on or in the stars, for at their temperatures all but the simplest of molecules are broken apart. Stars can carry the evolution of matter no further than the production of 92 elements. Theirs were the grand and spectacular endeavors; the delicate and subtle synthesis must be left to others (see Table 1).

Now enter the humble planets: small, cool, dark parasites always needing a nearby star for a source of energy. Debris left over after stars were formed, they are merely rock chips lying in the dark surrounding the brightly blazing sculp-

TABLE 1. The Early Universe

Era	Start	End	Temperature at Start	Density at Start (gm/cm^3)
1. Chaos	0	10^{-44} sec	infinite	infinite
2. Cosmic Parents	10^{-44} sec	10 sec	10^{33}	10^{94}
3. Golden Egg	10 sec	10^6 years	10^{10}	10^4
4. Stellar	10^6 years	continuing	3000	10^{-21}
1980	—	—	2.7	10^{-30}

ture. But we need not be apologetic for our diminutive home. On the green flanks of the earth have appeared creatures lying far beyond the procreative ability of the hot stars. Responsibility now shifts to the planets which can provide the substrate for the emergence of thought in the universe.

As when the passengers of a train become aware of the train when it rounds a curve, evolution catches sight of itself through human consciousness. As Teilhard de Chardin describes it: "The consciousness of each of us is evolution looking at itself and reflecting on itself." The residue of a supernova living on a tiny planet thus becomes a mirror for the universe.

The three billion human creatures living on the earth's surface weigh approximately 150 billion kilograms. The solar system has a mass of 2×10^{30} kilograms. Humankind accounts for a mere one part in 10^{19} of the local world. Inconsequential by mass, size, and brightness, human consciousness is a tiny reflecting chip into which the universe peers.

The universe has been nudged in the direction of consciousness by the convergence of space-time. Just as the convergent structure of a wine glass draws condensing moisture together down the stem, so the convergence of the structure of space-time causes matter to form clumps. The mutual attraction of matter which we call gravity results from that convergence. In flat space-time there would be no gravity and no tendency for clustering and in negatively curved space-time matter would be self-repulsive.

That nudge, however, has been slight. Mankind can not live at the only focus of convergent lines of space-time, at the only mouth of the only funnel. We have been burned too often in the past to believe that sort of anthropocentric presumption. To imagine that we and only we could have emerged from chaos is to eliminate the infinitely creative possibilities of the beginning of the world. The emergence of human consciousness must be more than the emergence of a plant from the information contained in the chromosomes of a seed or more than the manufacture of a watch by an external watchmaker using a preconceived design.

We certainly do not understand that process of self-transformation in all of its detail. Non-equilibrium, change, convergence, and environmental selection were ingredients. There must have been incessant experimentation, as billions upon billions of combinations of matter and energy were attempted, most of which were wretched failures. There must have been vast amounts of time spent in exploring and groping, in the words of Teilhard, "trying everything so as to find everything."

The initial potential has not been exhausted. Work remains for us to do, and Kazantzakis in *The Saviors of God* has written a set of instructions for the journey which lies ahead. God needs the midwifery of man to refine and transmute matter into spirit, facts into theory, and chaos into order. "Within the province of our ephemeral flesh all of God is imperiled. He cannot be saved unless we save him with our struggles . . ."

Kazantzakis suggests that in order to free the spirit of God we must realize that each of us is solely responsible for the salvation of the entire universe. A big order, but who else can express the uniqueness which is contained in the atoms of our minds? Love, curiosity, and joy are forces which urge us on in our struggle.

And the end? We can not be certain whether it will be death by ice or by fire. Kazantzakis sees a pyre burning brightly ahead: "Flame will surely come one day to purify the earth. Fire is the first and final mask of my God."

11. A Day in the Life of Brahma

What we call the beginning is often the end
And to make an end is to make a beginning
The end is where we start from.
T. S. Eliot, "Little Gidding"

In the *Upanishads* there is the story of an amoeba-like god who divides himself to become all the variety of creation. Having discovered that mitosis is so much fun, he can not resist endless self-transformation. He stretches himself further and further and then, like a broken rubber band, there are two gods . . . then four . . . then eight. . . . There is no limit to the number of forms he can take; all the diversity of the universe results from one initial god: not atoms and galaxies made by god, but atoms and galaxies which are god.

. . . in the beginning this universe was but the Self in the form of a man. He looked around and saw nothing but himself. Thereupon his first thought was, "It is I!" . . .

Then he was afraid . . . he considered, "Since there is nothing here but myself, what is there to fear?" Whereupon the fear departed; for what should have been feared? It is only to a second that fear refers.

However, he still lacked delight. He desired a second. He was just as large as a man and woman embracing. This Self then divided himself into two parts; and with that, there were a master and mistress. He united with her, and from that mankind arose.

She, however, reflected: "How can he unite with me,

who am produced from himself? Well, then, let me
hide!" She became a cow, he a bull and united with
her; and from that cattle arose. She became a mare, he a
stallion; she an ass, he a donkey, and united with her;
and from that solid-hoofed animals arose. She became a
goat, he a buck; she a sheep, he a ram and united with
her; and from that goats and sheep arose. Thus he
poured forth all pairing things, down to the ants.

In the mythology of Hinduism, the universe is a game of
masquerade in which nothing truly new ever appears. The
dividing god can not improve upon the perfection of creation because he is already perfect: he is god. There is nowhere to progress, for he is already there. It is ever good
and ever sufficient.

As aeon after aeon sweep by, the game continues because
there are always new masks and new costumes which he
can try on. He experiments with different roles, puts on different masks, and is ever surprising himself or frightening
himself in the mirror. He then breaks out in laughter when
he discovers himself behind the mask: "Oh so it's been you
all along, you old trickster!" The new roles are not better,
nor more highly evolved, nor more skillfully fashioned.
There are always infinitely more roles to be enjoyed and so
the game goes on for eternity.

In Hindu cosmology there never was a time when the god
was not either inventing new games or resting between
games. The quantities of time which are involved in the
Hindu stories of creation are as immense as those measures
of time and distance we use in astronomy. There is a remarkable story concerning the god Vishnu which expresses
the vastness of the cosmic arena in which the Hindu deities
work out the destinies of the world. The story describes an
event which occurred near the dawn of the present day of
Brahma, a little less than 4,320,000,000 years ago, when
Vishnu took on the incarnation of a boar to fight the serpent
king.

The earth had just been formed and like a lotus on the quiet surface of a lake she rested, fresh and fair on the waters of the cosmic ocean. But out of the ocean rose the giant serpent of the abyss, and took the newly blossomed earth down into its lowest, darkest depths. The unfolding of creation was thus endangered by the serpent who lies in ambush to return order back to chaos.

It was at this point that Vishnu became a giant boar and plunged into the depths of the ocean. There he found the serpent king holding the newly formed earth as his prisoner. Battling the serpent he rescued the earth and carried her up to the surface of the ocean while she clung to his tusk.

While he is carrying the goddess mother earth up through the waters, he makes the startling and revealing comment: ". . . every time I carry you this way. . . ." This could not have been the first time he performed the rescue nor shall it be the last. The crisis which led Vishnu to become the boar will repeat again and again, just as the earth dies each winter and is rescued by the sun each spring. Vishnu dives, battles the dark serpent power, and then re-emerges; he dives again, again he battles, and again he re-emerges carrying the earth; and yet again and again; up and down, cycle after cycle without end, for billions upon billions of aeons, marking out a rhythm in which our paltry time on the earth is but a brief grace note.

The rhythm is that of Brahma's breathing. With each breath Brahma creates and then destroys the universe, and the cosmos cycles from birth to death and then back to birth as he continues breathing in and out. A thousand breaths comprise the day of Brahma, which is known as the Kalpa.

Each separate breath-universe created by Brahma follows an inevitable course of decay and disintegration, for in this as in the physicist's world, entropy inexorably rises as time wears on.

Each universe is divided into four *yugas* named after the four throws of the Indian game of dice (see Table 2). The

TABLE 2. Hindu Cosmochronology

Yuga	Duration (years)
Krita	1,728,000
Treta	1,296,000
Dvapara	864,000
Kali	432,000
	4,320,000 = one mahayuga = one breath of Brahma

1000 mahayugas = one day of Brahma = 1 Kalpa

first, the Krita Yuga corresponding to a throw of four, is the most perfect; virtue and spirituality reign. But soon the processes of decay begin their work and the initial impulse of creation loses momentum. During the Treta Yuga, corresponding to the throw of three, the universe is sustained by only three-fourths of its original virtue. During the next yuga, the Dvapara Yuga, there is an ominous balance between order and disorder. The semi-divine status of society has vanished; no longer does the natural perfection of the world energize people. Men are blinded by passion for earthly goods or fame, growing mean and acquisitive. Finally the universe enters the final stage, the Kali Yuga. Corresponding to the losing throw of the game of dice, it is the age in which we now live. Full of war and hatred, the universe clings in this dark age to a mere quarter of its original grace. Finally overwhelmed by strife, the universe expires; the breath is finished; the turn of the wheel is complete.

At the end of the day of Brahma, after one thousand such cycles, Vishnu, the Supreme Being, is responsible for destroying the cosmos from the level of Brahma down to that of the smallest elementary particle. The night of Brahma lasts as long as the day, and at the dawn of a new Kalpa, Brahma reappears sitting on a lotus which has emerged from the navel of Vishnu.

The manner of death of the universe is described in numerous ways in Indian mythology. One account given in the Puranas describes Vishnu as an armed warrior, mounted on a white horse, furnished with wings and adorned with jewels, waving over his head with one hand the sword of destruction and holding a disc in the other. When the horse stamps the earth with his right fore-leg, the tortoise, which supports the serpent Shesha on whose hood rests the world, falls into the ocean and thus all the wicked inhabitants of the world are destroyed.

In the *Bhagbata*, the end is described as an "age of destruction . . . so horrible that during it the clouds never fall on the earth as drops of rain for one hundred years. The people then find no food to eat . . . and are compelled to eat one another. Being thus overpowered by what is wrought by time, the men gradually lead themselves to utter destruction."

Destruction of the world by fire and water is a trustworthy and time-tested technique. The climate of India is used as a pattern, and the amplitude of the cycles of intense heat and torrential rain is increased. Vishnu pours his infinite energy into the sun, and the earth dries up, splitting and cracking like a desiccated fruit. The surface features and the atmosphere are consumed in a great conflagration, leaving only lifeless ash. Then Vishnu lets loose a torrential rain to quench the smoldering ash and the scorched earth sinks below the primordial ocean, the same ocean from which it emerges at the start of each new cycle. The moon and the stars dissolve and the water becomes a dark and shoreless ocean in which the sleeping form of Vishnu floats.

The sleeping god dreams throughout the long night, and in one of those dreams a fantastic experience happens to a holy man known as Markendeya. In the dream he is wandering about India visiting cities and shrines all of which lie within the interior of Vishnu's sleeping body. The god sleeps with his mouth open, snoring away in the otherwise silent night of Brahma, and Markendeya has the missfortune to fall out of the god's mouth. Terrified, he plunges into the dark ocean. At first he does not see the sleeping form of Vishnu and, totally confused, he attempts to swim in that alien ocean. He wonders if his previous experiences had been a dream from which he has just awakened; or perhaps the black waters in which he is struggling are the ingredients of his current dream. But the water is too wet and cold to be a mere dream. Then he sees the form of the sleeping god, floating like the *Queen Elizabeth* with engines stilled and lights out. He swims over to Vishnu, clears his throat, and begins to ask what is going on. But suddenly Vishnu opens his mouth wider, grunts, and swallows the bewildered Markendeya. Back again in Vishnu's dream he finds himself in familiar surroundings, haunted with memories of that black ocean in which he nearly drowned. Which is the dream and which is real? Of one thing we can be certain: the full world is more than its solid and unchanging aspect, for that which appears substantial is always transformed in the dusk which concludes the day of Brahma.

Another variation of this theme that our reality is but a dream of a sleeping god comes from Miguel de Unamuno with a curious twist. He asks if Christian prayer and ritual may not perhaps be attempts on our part to make God drowsy, so that He does not awaken and terminate that dream which is our reality. As ever, the proper course of action is difficult to discover: should one whisper and tiptoe around the house fearful that our only identity comes from the dream of our sleeping parents, or as with parents such as Rangi and Papa do they need to be wakened and separated in order to allow change and evolution to continue?

The modern counterpart of the eternal round of Vishnu's waking and dreaming is the oscillating universe. Each collapse of the universe may be followed by another expansion. If the universe is a closed system, neither losing energy to nor taking energy from the outside, these oscillatory cycles of expansion and contraction may continue unabated for eternity. During the first half of each cycle space expands due to the energy of the initial explosion. Unable to overcome the self-gravity of all the matter and energy, the system of galaxies eventually reverses its expansion and during the second half of the cycle falls back upon itself. The falling heavens are filled with blue-shifted galaxies, and chaos returns.

That the universe will collapse in the future now seems unlikely. The density of matter averaged throughout the universe does not appear to be sufficient to stop expansion. The galaxies running away from us will continue to run away until they are dark and invisible cinders; even then in the night of the universe expansion will continue. But, in this presumptuous game of cosmology, the final word has not yet been said. Anything is still possible: sufficient mass may be hidden somewhere in space in quantities sufficient to draw the galaxies back onto themselves in a few hundred billion years. If that occurs, the collapse of the universe will be similar to the collapse that occurs in a black hole, and in its alien darkness we encounter yet another version of the end of the universe. The idea of a black hole was first advanced by Simon Laplace in 1796 when he recognized that on a highly compact and dense object, gravity might be so strong that light could not escape. In 1939, J. Robert Oppenheimer and H. Snyder developed the modern theory for the black hole using the ideas of General Relativity. They predicted that large stars with masses five or ten times the mass of the sun could collapse under their own gravity and turn themselves into holes from which nothing could escape. Since there are many stars in our galaxy with such mass, it seemed possible that many black holes had already formed.

Our sun, like all the stars in the sky, lies poised between fire and ice. The opposing forces of expansion and contraction are in equilibrium as the inward directed force of gravity is neutralized by the outward directed pressure of the sun's hot gasses. These two processes are now in balance, and will remain so balanced for another four billion years.

When the sun loses its ability to generate sufficient heat in its center to maintain this balance, gravity will become the dominant force and the sun will slowly move in upon itself. The forces arising from the dislike of one electron for another, known as the Pauli Exclusion Principle, will prevent the sun from collapsing into an object smaller than a white dwarf, approximately 100 times smaller than the present sun.

More massive stars possessing much stronger forces of gravity can not utilize the Pauli Exclusion Principle to prevent collapse, and the large star continues collapsing beyond the white dwarf stage until another source of support is discovered. Intermediate mass stars can take advantage of the Exclusion Principle as applied to neutrons, and in the shape of dense, rapidly spinning neutron stars, these objects will remain balanced until the end of the universe.

Still larger stars will collapse to densities which are so great that no known force is able to counteract the pull of gravity. Those stars, once their nuclear fuel is exhausted, collapse without limit. They may pass through the supernova stage when a large fraction of their mass is expelled in an explosion. But if the remaining mass is large enough, the material will continue its downward pursuit of itself, until the matter leaves the world of sight and touch, leaving behind only its gravitational pull.

Both matter and light use up energy when they escape from a gravitational field. The thrown ball slows down in its upward flight and eventually stops in its movement. When light loses energy, instead of slowing it shifts its color and becomes redder. Light from the sun is slightly red-shifted; that from a white dwarf is even more red-shifted, and that from a neutron star would be more shifted still. At the edge of a black hole, its event horizon, the strength of the gravitational field is so strong that escaping light has an *infinite red-shift*. This simply means that no energy can escape; light does not exist when it has an infinitely long wavelength. The object has thus lost all chance of communicating with the outside world. It has left its mark on surrounding space in the form of a gravitational field: a gravitational leer existing in the distortion of space and time.

We can only speculate upon what happens inside the event horizon of the collapsing star. Time is slowed down in a gravitational field compared to the time outside and time stops at the event horizon. An object falling into a black hole would seem to take an infinite time to cross the horizon as seen by an outside observer. Since such a falling object would be using up an infinite quantity of time to fall, there would not be time enough for it to come back out, and hence it would be eternally kidnapped by the gravity of the black hole.

The actual scenario for collapse is probably a re-run in reverse of the expansion of the universe that took place at the end of Chaos. Matter as it falls and encounters increasingly constricted space, will be transformed into particles with increasing mass and decreasing size, until eventually the ultimate particle, the archeon, is generated. Beyond that stage the archeons fall into their own black holes; they are black holes within a black hole. We can not follow the trail any further with our physics for all is sunk in Chaos.

In 1973 the first evidence for the existence of a black hole in our galaxy was obtained by R. Giacconi and co-workers. In an x-ray source in the constellation of Cygnus, known as Cygnus X-1, bursts of x-rays come from an object that is not visible in ordinary light. It appears to be a member of a double star system, having as a companion a blue supergiant star with a mass 25 times that of the sun. The supergiant moves back and forth in the sky over a distance of 5 million kilometers with a period of 5.6 days. The x-ray source must have a large mass in order to swing so large a star over such a great distance in such a short time. Its mass has been estimated to lie between 5 and 10 solar masses, and an ordinary star or even a dwarf with such a mass should be easily visible. The most reasonable interpretation is that a black hole is drawing off material from the supergiant, and bursts of x-rays are generated as that material is squeezed by the immense gravity existing just outside the event horizon of the black hole.

There may be many more black holes in our galaxy than this one in Cygnus. There are five more x-ray sources which are good candidates for double star systems containing black holes. Measurements of the orbits of stars moving around the center of our galaxy suggest that there may be large amounts of undetected dark matter in our galaxy. The black and thirsty cinders left over after the collapse of massive stars appear good sources of such invisible matter. Scattered throughout our galaxy black holes may thus occur in numbers rivaling that of ordinary visible stars.

Black holes have extraordinary fascination because of their exotic nature. They present extraordinary hazards to future galactic adventurers. But they can be atrociously monotonous. For, in the jargon of black hole physicists, they have "no hair." The boundary between the black hole and our universe is as smooth as a baldpate. Regardless of what is flushed down the hole, the resulting object is almost always the same. All details of the original material are destroyed by the forces of gravity that exist beyond the event horizon. Only total mass, electric charge, and angular momentum distinguish one black hole from another. Be the material originally a gaggle of geese, a bevy of sky larks, or a truck load of concrete, the resulting black hole will display no memory of the original character of the ingredients.

In this indistinguishability of black holes, there is a curious transcendence of the conservation laws of physics. In the past it has always been very useful to count the number of individual particles involved in various reactions, such as collisions or radioactive decay. The total number of heavy particles (protons and neutrons) is conserved: the number before the reaction equals the number left over after the reaction is completed. Similarly, the number of light particles (electrons and neutrinos) is conserved. Regardless of the energies involved or the specific details of the reaction, this quality of lightness or heaviness is carried along during the process. Heaviness of a proton seems to count; the electron seems to remember its light-ness.

But how long will such heaviness and lightness be pre-served in a changing universe? We have already seen that the ideas of Mach led to the prediction of a varying mass of individual particles due to a changing coupling between the universe and the particles. Here we return to a similar con-clusion using entirely different arguments. Since the distin-guishing mass of a particle is lost in the black hole, its mass appears to be a transient attribute destined to be inciner-ated along with everything else at the end of the world. The fact that particles are specifically electrons or protons ap-pears to be of secondary importance.

The mass of a particle may be a remembrance of time past. The particle may in fact be a fossil of events which oc-curred early in the life of our universe. For instance, a piece of coal is such a remembrance, a relic of ancient times on our planet when as a result of a particular set of pho-tochemical processes, light and air and earth were fused together into a fragile grouping of atoms. But when that chunk of coal is tossed onto a fire, much of that memory is destroyed as its molecular composition is altered. With suf-ficient heat it will be returned to the original atoms of car-bon, oxygen, and nitrogen. Its appearance as coal is merely a transient quality of those atoms.

The iron grate upon which the chunk of coal burns is equally a relic of ancient processes which occurred before our sun was born. So, too, that iron can be changed back to its original protons and electrons if it is subjected to a tem-perature near 7 billion degrees. And now it appears that even those protons and electrons can lose their identity in the melting pot of the black hole. They too seem to be relics of an earlier time, the primordial fireball of creation. If and when the universe collapses into that searing mirror image of the fireball of creation, all the present distinctions will be transcended.

The mind-addling collapse of the universe represented by the black hole demonstrates more dramatically than all the apothegms of Heraclites that the only law of the universe is the law of mutability. There is in our cosmos nothing so solid and permanent that it does not suffer change.

As in the cosmic egg of our beginnings, so in the black hole of the end, all is flux. The dissolution of matter at the termination of the Kali Yuga and the coming into being of the universe of the start of the Krita Yuga are but different aspects of eternal change. In that Heraclitean fire which is our end and our beginning and which lies at the edge of time, "fire will judge and convict all things."

12. The Cosmic Lottery

And the lotus rose, quietly, quietly,
The surface glittered out of heart of light,
And they were behind us, reflected in the pool.
Then a cloud passed and the pool was empty.
                    T. S. Eliot, "Burnt Norton"

"I come from a vertiginous country where the lottery
forms a principal part of reality." Thereupon Jorge
Borges introduces the chaos and madness that mark the
world he describes in his story *The Babylonian Lottery*. Living in a universe ruled by disorder and irrationality, man as
portrayed by Borges lies helpless before the uncertainties of
chance. The events of his world are as unpredictable as hiccups. His story of the lottery describes the history of a capricious organization which injects complete and total irrationality into the lives of the people of Babylon.

The result of the functioning of the lottery is an "almost
atrocious variety" in the lives of the inhabitants of the city.
The narrator of the story, like all men in Babylon, has been
"a proconsul; like all a slave." He has known "omnipotence, opprobrium, jail." He has found himself invisible,
shrieking with horror but not heard. Above all, he has
known uncertainty.

The nightmare of Borges is deeper and more complete
than that of Kafka whose story *The Castle* may be viewed as
another literary version of the uncertainty principle of
quantum mechanics. Kafka does not go far enough; he is
anguished in being excluded from participation in an order
which exists. There must be reason within the castle, yet
nothing but unreason surrounds him as he waits in the
town at the bottom of the hill. Borges reaches closer to the

modern spirit of quantum mechanics when he proclaims that even a hidden order does not exist: chaos rules the castle also.

The horror of the irrational is for Borges coexistent with the entire cosmos. Chaos reaches from the smallest of the microcosm and the largest of the macrocosm. In Babylon one can never be certain of the nature of events which dominate one's life. Never can one distinguish between an act which would obey a divine command or falsify it, nor can anyone be certain that there is such a thing as a divine command as opposed to blind chance. Chance is so pervasive in the city that one can not even be certain that chance is operating.

Is it, for instance, chance or conscious intent that a scribe who draws up a contract rarely fails to introduce an erroneous fact? Is it the spinning of an unseen wheel of chance which determines whether the buyer of a dozen amphoras of Damascus wine will find one of them containing a talisman or a viper?

The lottery is run by men who are secretive beyond all reason. Their agents can not be identified. The manner by which they carry out the results of the lottery is unknown; the results of the drawings are always camouflaged.

There was a time in Babylon when people had to purchase lottery tickets. But now everyone, rich and poor alike, is serviced without charge by the company. "The orders which it is continually sending out do not differ from those lavishly issued by imposters. Besides, who can ever boast of being a mere imposter? The inebriate who improvises an absurd mandate, the dreamer who suddenly awakes to choke the woman who lies at his side to death, do they not both perhaps carry out a secret decision by the Company?"

The narrator cannot even be certain that the company even exists: "There is one conjecture, spoken from the mouths of masked heresiarchs, to the effect that the Company has never existed and never will." So thoroughly impregnated with chance, Borges's reality is impenetrable by reason.

The uncertainty principle of quantum mechanics suggests a similar disorder in the foundation of the world. There seems to be no way of predicting the fluctuations of individual atomic phenomena. The irregular fluctuations of the velocity and position of an electron are unlike all other types of fluctuations with which we are familiar in our world. The number of children born, the number of storks building nests on chimney-tops, the number of automobile accidents fluctuate from day to day, but in principle one can trace the details of these fluctuations to contributing causes. In contrast, the fluctuations of the electron can never be traced to prior causes. Each individual event is an entirely arbitrary phenomenon, having no causal relationship to anything that exists now or to anything that has occurred in the past. Our world of quantum mechanics seems not basically different from that of Babylon, "nothing more than an infinite game of chance." We are the products of a series of lawless, irrational fluctuations which "make sense" only if we consider them statistically. We are able to predict how a collection of phenomena will behave, but never are we able to make predictions about individual events.

There is no aspect of the theory of quantum mechanics which allows a prediction of the precise outcome of any particular experiment. The electron, for instance, is viewed as being a superposition of an infinite number of possible electrons and only during the act of measurement does the ball of the roulette wheel drop and thereby actualize one of the electron states.

For a crude example we return to the act of tossing coins on a table. The coins and the table have the potential of lying together in a variety of states. It is impossible to predict the outcome of any one particular act of tossing the coins on the table: two heads, two tails, one head and one tail. All one can do is to speak of probabilities. After, say, twenty tosses, it is likely that five will have been two heads, five will have been two tails, and then will have been one head and one tail. Each individual toss actualizes one particular combination of coins and each can only be predicted on the basis of a certain probability less than unity.

Similarly we can speak about actualizing the potentialities of a beam of electrons which are hitting a target. The electrons are released by a hot tungsten cathode and are focused by a configuration of electric fields which act on the electrons much the same ways as a lens acts on a beam of light. The electrons are sent to a target which may be a photographic plate which is exposed upon being hit by an electron. The resulting pattern on the photographic plate is not just a manifestation of the potentiality of the electron beam, but of the potentialities of the entire situation: the electron, the tungsten filament, the electron lens, the target, the walls of the container, the detailed structure of the emulsion, and the experimenter overseeing the experiment. The result which is described as "the electron" is a partial representation of the entire experiment and everything even remotely connected with it. The particular electron of the experiment does not exist apart from that particular experiment. The electron is an abstraction of the total situation. A slightly different experimental situation would produce something different.

The electron thus is different each time one looks at it; not only may the experimental situation be different, but each electron has only a certain probability of appearing even in identical experiments. Coins are always approximately coins, being larger than the scale at which quantum mechanical effects are important. But the small electrons are ever elusive and playful, always involved in unpredictable change.

Our world is rich and our interaction with it so full of surprise because of this fundamental unpredictability of matter and energy. From our perspective the world is disordered, but it is precisely because of disorder that the world is always new and possesses a future which is different from the past.

A fascinating symbol for this sort of creative disorder is the Trickster. Among the North American Indians of the Plains he was usually the Coyote. For the woodland tribes of the North and East, he appeared as the Great Hare, the Master Rabbit who reappeared also as Br'er Rabbit. A raven, blue jay, and Reynard the Fox are some of his other apparitions.

Cunning, lecherous, always the fool, Coyote was man's benefactor as the Prometheus who stole fire from the Fire People and accidentally burned himself in the process. He represents the ever-present ferment of a world which is always bubbling away, never predictable in precise detail, but extraordinarily fecund and prolific. While the earth had not yet crystallized and much could still be fashioned out of the primordial stuff, the shadowy figure of the creator traveled about, according to the Blackfeet of Montana, making people and arranging things. "He came from the south, traveling north making animals and birds as he passed along. He made the mountains, prairies, timber, and brush first. So he went along, traveling northward making things as he went, putting rivers here and there, and falls on them, putting red paint here and there in the ground—fixing up the world as we see it today." In this story he is well behaved; in many others he is the epitome of disorder, possessing what the Tibetan Buddhists refer to as crazy wisdom, creating because he is always doing something. It doesn't particularly matter precisely what he is doing or whether it has an obvious purpose. His vitality and craziness are sufficient.

Some of his more disorderly conduct is evident in the following rich and earthy tale:

When he was one day wandering about aimlessly, he heard someone say, "Anyone who chews me will defecate; he will defecate." "Well," said Trickster, "why is this person talking in this manner?" He moved in the direction from which the voice had come and then he heard it again. Looking around, he saw a bulb on a bush. "I know very well," he said to himself, "that if I chew this I will not defecate." So he took it, put it into his mouth, chewed, swallowed it, and went on.

"Well," he said, "where is the bulb that talked so much? How could such an object influence me in the least? When I feel like defecating I shall do so, and no sooner." But while he was speaking he began to break a little wind. "Well," he thought, "I guess this is what it meant. It said, though, that I would defecate and I'm just breaking a little wind. In any case, I am a great man even if I do expel a little gas." Then it happened again, and this time it was really strong. "Well indeed! How foolish I was! Perhaps this is why they call me the Fool!" It happened again, very loudly, and this time his rectum began to smart. Next time he was propelled forward. "Well, well," he thought defiantly, "it may give me a little push but it will never make me defecate." It happened again and this time the hind part of his body was lifted into the air and he landed on his knees and hands. "Well, just go ahead, do it again!" he cried. "Do it again!" It did, and he went far up into the air, landing flat on his stomach. He began to take the matter seriously. He grabbed a log, and both he and the log were sent into the air. Coming down, the log was on top and he was nearly killed. He grabbed a poplar tree; it held, but his feet flew into the air and nearly broke his back. Next, the tree came up by the roots. He grabbed a large oak tree; this held, but again his feet flew into the air. Trickster ran to a village and contrived to have all the lodges piled on top of him, together with the people, dogs, and everything else. His explosion scattered the camp in all directions and the people, coming down, shouted angrily at each other, while the dogs howled. Trickster just laughed at them until his insides were sore. But then he began to defecate.

Here, in the form of the Trickster, is a force careless of taboos and decorum, creative because he is alive, chaotic because he does not fit into the old molds. As he bumbles along, he generates both outrageous mistakes and gorgeous creations. Ultimately as unpredictable and irrational as the electron, he embodies the same intuition about an irrational world as does the Uncertainty Principle.

Let us try to penetrate deeper into the irrational world of quantum mechanics. One of the most astonishing developments of quantum physics in the last twenty years is the prediction and verification of the fluctuation of the electromagnetic field in a vacuum. It was essentially a demonstration of the previously unsuspected depth and extent to which the microcosm is irrational. Consider the single solitary electron moving through empty space. In the absence of any forces acting upon it, it should follow a straight line in flat space. If space is curved, it will follow a geodesic. If the electron is in a hydrogen atom, it will follow a path dictated by the steady electric field of the charged nucleus. A steady electric field should mean a smooth and peaceful voyage for the electron in orbit about the nucleus. Instead, it turns out that the electron wiggles incessantly as if it were being subjected to a randomly varying electric field superimposed upon the steady field. That superimposed electric field produces an observed change in the energy of an electron in an atom, known as the Lamb-Rutherford shift. The specific details of that fluctuating electric field are totally unpredictable by modern quantum theory. Only the average effect can be predicted theoretically and that agrees very well with the observed measured shift.

The fluctuating electric field introduces a steady noise in our background, a hum as it were which eliminates any possibility of pure silence. The path of the electron controlled by this erratic field lies beyond our powers of prediction.

Not just the electric field, but all fields and their associated forces contain such irrational noise (see Figure 8).

FIGURE 8.

All systems whether they be weights suspended on springs, vibrating molecules, or electrons in atoms contain these quantum mechanical fluctuations. Thus a collection of atoms in a molecule will continue to vibrate even at absolute zero with a so-called zero point energy. Since there is a minimum level of vibration below which no system can sink, quantum mechanics has eliminated quiescence from our universe. After the last photon has been radiated by an atom and the electrons have reached the ground state of the atom, the electrons still move and still have energy. Similarly, the vibrating electrons and protons in a white dwarf star will continue to vibrate even as they go into that dark night of the black dwarf; both atom and star are brothers to Sisyphus, caught in eternal motion without respite.

Even a perfect vacuum, free of all matter and energy, contains fluctuations of fields and particles. Out of the vacuum electrons, positrons, and photons (or other particles and their antiparticles) can emerge spontaneously, remaining only briefly in our world before they annihilate each other.

Finally the fluctuations do not just involve matter and energy, for the very scaffolding of space appears to shake. Superimposed upon the large-scale geometry of space are random quantum fluctuations like small ripples on large waves. In everyday circumstances, the fluctuations in the geometry of space are completely negligible. Only at the sub-microscopic scale do these fluctuations become significant. At that level, space is constantly closing in upon itself and then opening up; the flat portions of space are not flat but constantly fluctuate between positive and negative curvature. It is as if the microcosm were a vibrating musical saw which is being flexed up and down. Microscopic black holes are being produced everywhere at random.

We have progressed an awesome distance from that passive and flat emptiness which used to lie between the atomic things of the world. The things are no longer things and the void is no longer empty. That inter-atomic void, free of matter and energy, once looked as smooth and featureless as the unblemished surface of a quiet pond. But now it appears that below its tranquil surface there simmers all the violence of the larger world, reduced in scale and increased in frequency.

These rising and falling fluctuations of space look like miniature universes, rising briefly and quietly like the lotus out of the pond, then falling back leaving no trace. Could our own universe be such a rising fluctuation of the vacuum? So large from the inside but inconsequential from the outside, our universe may be just one of countless random fluctuations of a greater vacuum field. The reader must be cautioned that these are speculations lying at the growing edge of modern astrophysics but they are worth our attention for they may relate to the largest question of them all concerning our presence in this universe. Why this particular fluctuation? If there are countless other rising and falling universes, why has mankind developed in this particular one, instead of the other ones, perhaps no less deserving than ours? The answer to these questions may be related to the extreme demands that are placed upon a universe which is to produce life.

Life, as we know it, needs the presence of elements heavier than hydrogen and time enough for these elements to form macro-molecules which can become self-aware. The production of heavy elements requires thermonuclear processes occurring in the interiors of stars. For many of these processes cooking times of a billion years or more are required. Such times are not available in much smaller universes which could go through cycles of expansion and contraction in less than a billion years. Likewise, life probably could not develop in larger universes with faster speeds of expansion. In those universes initially small density fluctuations could not grow to form galaxies because they would be stretched apart by the expansion of space faster than they could pull themselves together by self-gravity.

We can imagine a vast array of fluctuations of energy and space which have bubbled up out of some primordial vat. These other universes need not be sequential as is the case with the oscillating breath-universes of Brahma. Many may be occurring now at other locations in that background out of which our universe emerged. Not just larger or smaller than ours, the matter and energy within them may be distributed in a very irregular fashion. It is doubtful that another universe not possessing the large-scale homogeneity of our universe could become a container for man. The dense portions of an unhomogeneous universe would collapse into black holes too quickly for life to have formed in them and in the less dense regions matter would be too thinly distributed to be able to give birth to stars and galaxies. Moreover, if the values of the physical constants in another universe were different from those in ours, it is questionable that human life could arise.

We are approaching a rather astonishing conclusion: all of the physical characteristics of this universe may be determined by the fact that it is a mind-producing universe. Like tosses of coins, many other kinds of universes may have appeared, larger and smaller, thicker and thinner, but only this particular combination had the necessary mixture of energy and matter which could generate self-awareness.

Here is one of the most humbling myths of all. On these pages we have been exploring questions such as: why is the universe so large and expanding at a particular rate? why is it always out of equilibrium and why do all things change? According to quantum cosmology the answer to each question is remarkably simple. There have been many universes, but there has been only one home for man. We live in this particular cosmic structure because none other could have nurtured us. The shape, size, and details of this universe are established by the fact that it is man's home. What other creatures inhabit those other universes we cannot guess.

> We shall not cease from exploration
> And the end of all our exploring
> Will be to arrive where we started
> And know the place for the first time.
> T. S. Eliot, "Little Gidding"

About the Author

Dr. J. McKim Malville has received international recognition and honors for his work in the fields of astronomy and geophysics and their relationship to other disciplines. Now Professor and Chairman of the Department of Astro-Geophysics at the University of Colorado, Dr. Malville is also the author of numerous articles and a book, *A Feather for Daedalus: Explorations in Science and Myth.*

Bibliography

Chapter 1

Eliot, T. S. *The Complete Poems and Plays 1909–1950*. New York: Harcourt, Brace and Company, 1952.

Eiseley, L. *The Immense Journey*. New York: Random House, 1957.

Chapter 2

Bohm, D. *The Special Theory of Relativity*. New York: Benjamin, 1965.

Born, M. *Einstein's Theory of Relativity*. New York: Dover, 1962.

Einstein, A. *Relativity: The Special and General Theory*. New York: Crown, 1961.

Chapter 3

Hoyle, F. *From Stonehenge to Modern Cosmology*. San Francisco: W. H. Freeman, 1972.

Sachs, M. *The Field Concept in Contemporary Science*. Springfield: Charles C. Thomas, 1973.

Sciama, D. W. *The Physical Foundations of General Relativity*. Garden City: Doubleday, 1969.

Chapter 4

Bohm, D. *Causality and Chance in Modern Physics*. Philadelphia: University of Pennsylvania Press, 1957.

Chang, G. C. C. *The Buddhist Teaching of Totality*. University Park: The Pennsylvania State University Press, 1971.

Chapter 5

Bronowski, J. *The Identity of Man*. Garden City: The Natural History Press, 1965.
Campbell, J. *The Masks of God: Primitive Mythology*. New York: The Viking Press, 1969.
Kuhn, T. *The Structure of Scientific Revolutions* Chicago: The University of Chicago Press, 1970.
Ornstein, R. E. *The Psychology of Consciousness*. San Francisco: W. H. Freeman, 1972.

Chapter 6

Fraser, J. T. *The Voices of Time*. New York: Braziller, 1966.
Prigogine, I., Nocolis, G., and Babloyantz, A. "Thermodynamics of Evolution," *Physics Today*, 1972, 25: 23-28.

Chapter 7

Gal-Or, B. "The Crisis about the Origin of Irreversibility and Time Anisotropy," *Science*, 1972, 176:11–17.
Gott III, J. R., Gunn, J. E., Schramm, D. N., and Tinsley, B. M. "An Unbounded Universe?", *Astrophysical Journal*, 1974, 194:543–544.

Chapter 8

Alfven, H. *Worlds—Antiworlds*. San Francisco: W. H. Freeman, 1966.
Harrison, E. R. "The Early Universe," *Physics Today*, 1968, 21:31–39.
Long, C. H. *Alpha: The Myths of Creation*. New York: Braziller, 1963.

Chapter 9

Harrison, E. R. "The Early Universe," *Physics Today*, 1968, 21:31–39.

Long, C. H. *Alpha: The Myths of Creation*. New York: Braziller, 1963.

Merton, T. *Zen and the Birds of Appetite*, New York: New Directions, 1968.

Chapter 10

Kazantzakis, N. *The Saviors of God: Spiritual Exercises*. New York: Simon and Schuster, 1960.

Long, C. H. *Alpha: The Myths of Creation*. New York: Braziller, 1963.

Teilhard de Chardin, P. *The Phenomenon of Man*. New York: Harper, 1959.

Chapter 11

Henderson, J. L. and Oakes, M. *The Wisdom of the Serpent: The Myths of Death, Rebirth, and Resurrection*. New York: Macmillan, 1971.

Wheeler, J. A. "The Universe as Home for Man," *American Scientist*, 1974.

Zimmer, H. *Myths and Symbols in Indian Art and Civilization*. Princeton: Princeton University Press, 1946.

Chapter 12

Bohm, D. *Quantum Theory*. New York: Prentice-Hall, 1951.

Borges, J. L. *Ficciones*. New York: Random House, 1962.

Campbell, J. *The Masks of God: Primitive Mythology*. New York: The Viking Press, 1969.

Misner, C. W., Thorne, K. S. and Wheeler, J. A. *Gravitation*. San Francisco: W. H. Freeman, 1973.

Radin, P. *The Trickster*. New York: Philosophical Library, 1956.

Tyron, E. P. "Is the Universe a Vacuum Fluctuation?" *Nature*, 1973, 246:396–397.